FIELD STUDY MANUAL FOR OUTDOOR LEARNING

Margaret Milliken
Austin F. Hamer
Ernest C. McDonald

FIELD STUDY MANUAL FOR OUTDOOR LEARNING

by

Margaret Milliken
Associate Professor
Oregon State University

Austin F. Hamer
Assistant to State Director
Bureau of Land Management
Boise, Idaho

Ernest C. McDonald
Conservation Education Officer
U. S. Forest Service
Portland, Oregon

COMMUNICATION OF KNOWLEDGE

Burgess Publishing Company
426 South Sixth Street • Minneapolis, Minn. 55415

Printed in the United States of America

THIS MANUAL BELONGS TO:

____

THE NAME OF MY FIELD STUDY AREA IS:

____

THE LOCATION OF MY FIELD STUDY AREA IS:

____

THE DATES OF MY FIELD STUDY OBSERVATIONS WERE

______________ to ______________

ACKNOWLEDGEMENTS

The authors wish to thank the many persons who contributed their ideas and gave encouragement to the writing of this manual, particularly Bob L. Brown, deceased, U.S. Soil Conservation Service, for his contribution in the development of the ecological approach to field study. Grateful acknowledgement is made to Roy Johnson, U.S. Soil Conservation Service; Cal Geisler, Oregon State Game Commission; George Otte, U.S. Soil Conservation Service; Ron Rohweder, Oregon State Game Commission; and Ed Quan, Oregon State Board of Health, for their consultation and development of the information included in this manual.

We wish to express, also, our appreciation to the Oregon State Department of Forestry, Oregon State Game Commission, U.S. Forest Service, and the U.S. Soil Conservation Service resource agencies for their cooperation and furnishing of personnel to aid in experimentation and refinement of materials included in this manuscript. These illustrations are reprinted by permission of the Oregon State Game Commission.

A special and final acknowledgement is made to Harold Cramer Smith, staff artist for the Oregon Game Commission, and to Randi Lynn Bjornstad for illustrating the manual.

TABLE OF CONTENTS

INTRODUCTION

The land is a dynamic, living, ever-changing community of plants and animals dependent upon each other and the other resources for survival. The land does not stand still. Plants and animals are born, grow, and die to enrich and change the soil.

Organic material, thus added, affects the ability of the soil to absorb and hold water that is needed by plants and animals. As the structure of the soil is changed by decomposing plants and animals, new types of plants are able to grow. This, in turn, determines the kind and the number of animals that can live in an area.

The relationship of Man to the land has undergone many evident and complex changes. Man has used and converted the natural resources of the land to benefit his life. He has done things that have been bad for the land and bad for himself. Fortunately, he has also done other things which have been good for the land and himself.

If Man is to survive on earth, he must learn to live in harmony with the natural resources because he is totally dependent upon them. Past civilizations flourished when they had plenty of natural resources but vanished when the supply of resources dwindled.

This study of the effect of natural resources upon one another and also how Man influences and is influenced by the resources is called "Ecology." This term comes to us from two Greek words that mean "the study of the home."

The first step in learning how to live with our resources is to understand some of the ways that each natural resource affects the other resources. The chart on the following page shows some of the ways that resources affect each other.

HOW RESOURCES AFFECT EACH OTHER

SOIL	Water	Plants	Wildlife	Man
	Affects: Runoff Percolation into ground Underground storage Purity by filtration	Anchors plants Supplies water & minerals Affects where plants grow by: topography, elevation, soil depth, acidity or alkalinity of soil	Affects where animals live because of topography, elevation, availability of water and types of plants which grow	Affects: Productivity of soil Where man lives What he produces Economy based on location of resources Scenic values
WATER	Soil	Plants	Wildlife	Man
	Washes away soil Affects types of soil (swamp, desert) Helps break down soil by freezing, flowing, and seepage	Affects: Transpiration Where plants grow - swamp, hillside, rainfall, fog, snow, etc.	Affects: Aquatic animals Where animals live by their need for water and food	Provides scenic values, recreation Affects where man lives, (floods, drought), what he grows on soil
PLANTS	Soil	Water	Wildlife	Man
	Help rocks break into soil by root penetration Make organic fertilizer which enriches soils and absorbs water Hold soil in place Protect soil from rainfall	Make open spaces in soil for water penetration, tap roots Shade streams, keep water cool Use water in transpiration Purify water	Provide food, shelter, water in succulent plants fro drinking Give off O_2 for breathing	Provides: Forage for cattle Shelter Necessities & luxuries of life Recreation Shade Scenic values
WILDLIFE	Soil	Water	Plants	Man
	Make organic fertilizer Cause soil compaction Build beaver dams - percolate & hold H_2O in soil; prevent soil erosion	Pollute water Build beaver dams - flood control, water storage	Fertilize plants Carry seeds Give off CO_2 that plants need Destroy plants	Provide scenic values, recreation, hunting, fishing, livelihood in trapping Damage crops Kill livestock
MAN	Soil	Water	Plants	Wildlife
	Increases & decreases soil productivity Causes soil erosion Puts new lands in production Changes face of the earth Manages for his benefit	Stores water in dams Pollutes water Diverts water Uses more water than available in some areas Manages for his benefit	Grows new crops Eliminates natural plants Clears land of plants Harvests trees and grass Manages plants for his benefit	Harvests wildlife and natural predators Upsets nature's cycle of animals Manages for his benefit

FIELD STUDY INFORMATION

Before you begin your field study, there are some things that you need to know. This information will prepare you for your instructional periods on the field study area.

You and your class will have a certain area in the outdoors as your outdoor classroom. Near the center of the field study area, you will find an equipment box containing the special tools and instructions you need to do some of the activities in this manual. You will work on projects and activities as a class, in small groups or by yourself. All information will be recorded in this field study manual. You should record the date, time of day and what the weather was as you start the study of each resource. Each day, you and your class will participate in field study sessions about different resources. After studying about soil, water, plants and wildlife with your class, you will have an opportunity to experiment with activities that may be of interest to just you. Some of these activities are listed at the end of each chapter.

Here are a few general activities that might improve your field study area or help other students enjoy it more:

1. Make a nature and conservation trail, locating significant features and plants along the trail, and labeling them with self-explanatory signs.
2. Make a forest conservation mobile.
3. Fill in a gully that has eroded by building a check dam.
4. Place mulch around the roots of trees that are exposed and on trails and field study center to reduce soil compaction.
5. Make switch-back trails in your field study area to avoid soil erosion.
6. Make markers for trails.
7. Improve trails by clearing brush along edges of trail and by removal of rocks, logs, and slides on trail.
8. Build check dam of brush, rocks, sticks, etc., to hold back or slow down eroding hillsides.

EQUIPMENT YOU WILL NEED

In order to get the most from your field study sessions, you will need certain equipment. Here is a list of what you will need:

CLOTHING

Hiking shoes or boots (water repellent)
Long trousers (blue jeans, etc.)
Warm sweater or shirt

Rain jacket
Hat or waterproof head covering

EQUIPMENT

Required	Desirable
Pencil	Sun glasses
Field Study Manual	Magnifying glass
Pocket knife	Field glasses (binoculars)
Collecting bag	Camera and extra film
	Plant press
	Insect collection box
	Live animal trap
	Crayons

SPECIAL EQUIPMENT

1. pH soil testing kit - Contact a local soil scientist on how to obtain for use on page 23.
2. Dissolved O_2 testing kit - Contact a local water biologist on how to obtain for use on page 44.
3. Increment borer - Contact a local forester on how to obtain for use on page 68.

FIELD STUDY RULES

Whenever you go outside the classroom, there are some necessary rules to follow. The Outdoor School has certain rules too. Because you will be exploring our natural resources, it is necessary that you follow these rules for your protection and the protection and enjoyment of others.

1. Report to your instructor when entering or leaving the field study area.
2. Never wander off by yourself; always stay with another person.
3. Always carry and use tools properly to avoid injury.
4. Walk, don't run.
5. Avoid trampling, cutting, or marking plants.
6. Never dig up plants unless asked to do so by your instructor.
7. Only collect plant leaves or specimens as directed by your instructor.
8. Avoid disturbing or killing small animals such as insects, frogs and chipmunks.
9. When walking in the woods or on the trail, don't trip on roots, etc.
10. Don't let overhanging branches snap back and hit the person behind you.

MAPPING THE FIELD STUDY AREA

A. MEASURING DISTANCE
   1. Determining length of step
   2. Corrections for slope distance

B. TAKING COMPASS BEARINGS
   1. The compass
   2. Sighting a landmark and determining magnetic bearing
   3. Following a magnetic degree reading
   4. Cautions in using a compass

C. RECORDING DISTANCE, MAGNETIC COMPASS BEARINGS AND FIELD STUDY NOTES
   1. Example of recording field study notes

D. PARTS OF MAP
   1. Magnetic north arrow
   2. Map scale
   3. Map legend

E. DRAWING THE MAP

F. WATERSHED MAP OF AREA

MAPPING THE FIELD STUDY AREA

It is important to learn the boundaries and the location of the streams, rock outcroppings, difference in plant cover and wildlife habitat of your field study area. The best way to do this is to make a map. In order to make the map, you will have to measure distance, use a compass, record your bearings and then draw the map. The following instructions will help you.

A. MEASURING DISTANCE

You can measure the distance around your field study area by knowing the length of your step.

1. Instructions for determining length of step
   a. Mark off a 100 foot distance on level grade.
   b. Walk the distance 3 times; count your steps, and add them.

      Number of steps first time ________

      Number of steps second time ________

      Number of steps third time ________

      Total Steps ________

   c. Divide the total distance walked by the total number of steps you took to determine the number of feet in each step.

$$\frac{300\text{ feet}}{\text{(Total Distance Walked)}} \div \frac{\rule{3cm}{0.4pt}}{\text{(Total Steps Taken)}} = \frac{\rule{3cm}{0.4pt}}{\text{No. of feet in each step}}\text{ feet}$$

<u>Determine the following answers:</u>

No. of steps in 100 feet: (100 ft. ÷ Feet in step = Steps in 100')
Number of steps in 100 feet______________

No. of steps in $\frac{1}{4}$ mile: (1320 ft. ÷ Feet in step = Steps in $\frac{1}{4}$ mile)
Number of steps in $\frac{1}{4}$ mile ______________

No. of steps in 1 mile: (5280 ft. ÷ Feet in step = Steps in 1 mile)
Number of steps in 1 mile______________

As you measure distance in the field study area by walking, count the number of steps and multiply by the number of feet in each of your steps.

2. Corrections for measuring slope distances
   a. If you are measuring up-and-down slopes, you will have to correct the number of steps because map distances are always

figured for level ground. Walking over uneven terrain shortens your steps. Therefore, some steps are not counted on slopes. The following information will help you to determine step correction.

PERCENT SLOPE	ASCENDING Step	ASCENDING Skip	DESCENDING Step	DESCENDING Skip
60% (Very steep)	1	2	2	1
30% (Steep)	2	1	6	1
20% (Mod. steep)	3	1	11	1
10% (Gentle slope)	6	1	–	–

Example of use:

If, for example, you were on a steep slope of 30%, you would count the first two steps and not count the third step, count the next two steps and not count the third, etc.

B. MEASURING COMPASS BEARINGS

The four things to learn about using a compass for marking this map are:

Learning the parts of a compass
Learning to sight a landmark to determine your degree reading
Learning to follow a degree reading
Learning about cautions in using a compass

1. There are many compasses that you can use, but the Silva Compass is one of the easiest. There are three parts to the Silva Compass.
   a. Compass needle - The red end points to magnetic north and the white end points to south. Magnetic north is about 1400 miles away from true north. Since all permanent maps are made on a true north bearing, an adjustment must be made on the compass when surveying to make a map. This difference is called declination. Temporary maps, like the one you are making, are often drawn to magnetic north and no compass correction is necessary. You will make your map using magnetic bearing readings.

b. Compass housing, or dial, is round and encloses the magnetic needle. There is a degree circle marked on the outside of the dial. The space between each line marked on the housing represents two degrees. The four principal parts to a compass are: North (0° and 360°), East (90°), South (180°), and West (270°). The outline of the orienting arrow appears on the inside of the bottom of the housing. The compass housing moves.

c. The base plate is used to indicate the line of travel as shown by the "direction of travel arrow" on the plate. The base can also be used to measure distances on a map.

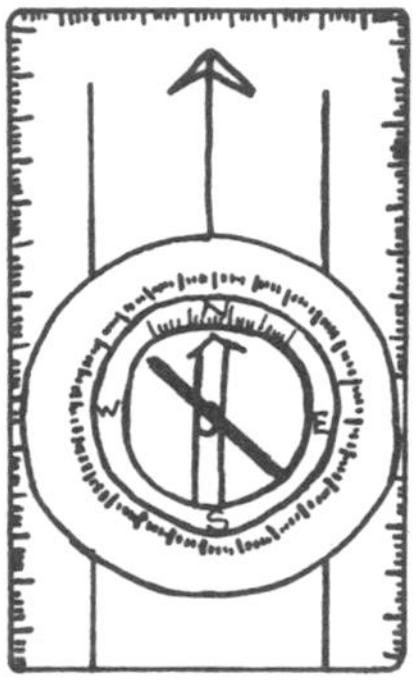

2. Sighting a landmark to determine your magnetic degree reading
   a. Face the landmark.
   b. With one hand, hold the compass waist high and level, with the direction of travel arrow pointing at the landmark.
   c. With the free hand, turn the dial until the orienting arrow (in the bottom of the dial) and the magnetic compass needle are in line (red end of magnetic needle must be at the arrow end of the orienting arrow). The two needles will then be pointing to magnetic North.
   d. Read and record the degree number which is directly over the direction of travel arrow.
3. Following a magnetic degree reading
   a. With one hand, hold the compass waist high and level with the direction of travel arrow pointing away from you.
   b. With the free hand, turn the dial until the desired degree number is directly over the direction of travel arrow.
   c. Keeping the compass level and still pointing away from you, rotate your body and the compass together until the magnetic compass needle and the orienting arrow are in line. (The red end of the magnetic needle must be at the arrow end of the orienting arrow). The two needles will then be pointing to magnetic North.

d. Look up from the direction of travel arrow and sight on a landmark in line with the direction of travel arrow.
e. Put compass away and walk straight to that point (keeping the landmark in sight). Count the number of steps and record.
f. Repeat the procedure for each degree number until you are at your destination.
g. Determine the total distance you walked by counting the number of steps you took and multiply by number of feet in each step.

4. Cautions in using a compass
   a. When following a degree reading, always follow the direction of travel arrow and not the direction of the needle.
   b. The compass is a delicate instrument; handle it carefully.
   c. Always follow the line indicated by the compass rather than relying on your judgment as to the direction.
   d. Remember the tree, rock or other object sighted on your line of sight. When in doubt, take another compass reading.
   e. Keep items containing steel or iron far enough away from the needles to avoid influencing it.
   f. Do not attempt to repair the compass except in emergencies.

C. RECORDING DISTANCES AND MAGNETIC COMPASS BEARINGS

You must record the magnetic compass bearings and the distances around the field study area as you take them.

EXAMPLE OF HOW TO RECORD YOUR FIELD SURVEY

DEGREE READING	FIELD NOTES	TOTAL DISTANCE		
		STEPS	FEET	MAP INCHES
135°	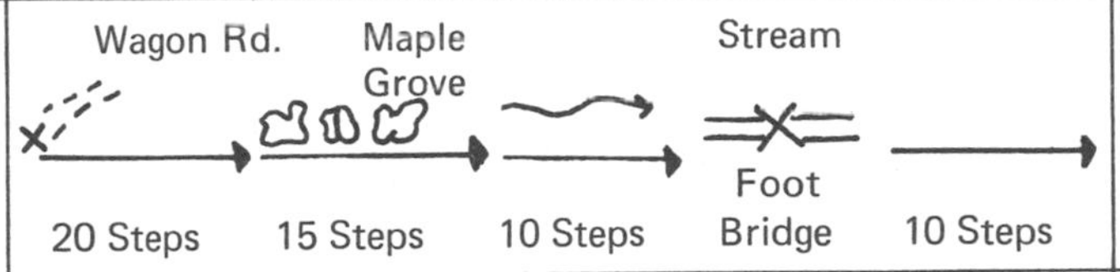 Wagon Rd. — Maple Grove — Stream — Foot Bridge; 20 Steps, 15 Steps, 10 Steps, 10 Steps	60 Steps		
270°	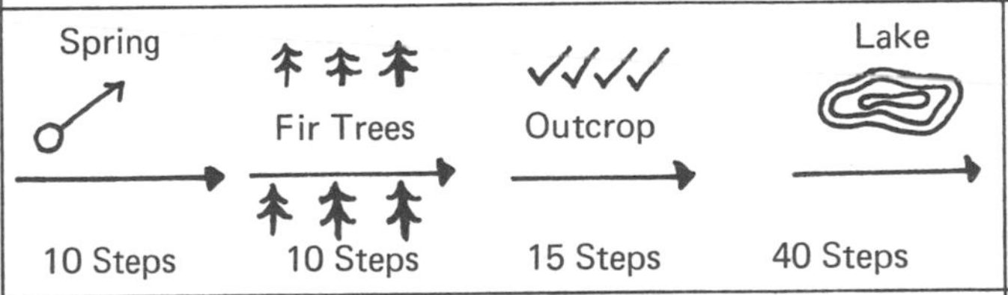 Spring — Fir Trees — Outcrop — Lake; 10 Steps, 10 Steps, 15 Steps, 40 Steps	75 Steps		
360°	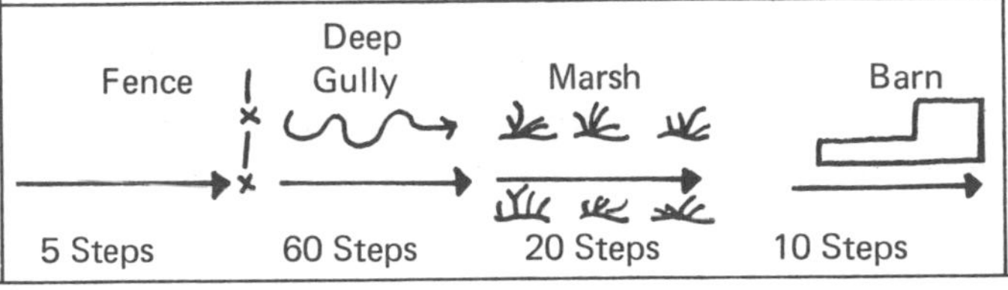 Fence — Deep Gully — Marsh — Barn; 5 Steps, 60 Steps, 20 Steps, 10 Steps	95 Steps		

The chart is an example of how to record your field survey notes. Note that land features are recorded in the field notes section (see map legend for symbols) as well as the degree reading and distance. You can record the number of steps as you take your notes and then change them into feet and finally map inches.

After you have determined the length of your step and how to take bearings with the compass, take and record on the field survey form below the degree readings and distances of the boundary of your field study area. Record in field notes, observations of stream crossings, trees, rocks, fences, etc. (See map legend for symbols, page 13).

RECORD OF FIELD SURVEY

DEGREE READING	FIELD NOTES	TOTAL DISTANCE		
		STEPS	FEET	MAP INCHES
Starting Point: ________°				

D. PARTS OF A MAP

Every map has three parts to help us interpret the map and locate ourselves in relation to the ground.

1. North Arrow
   Each map must have an arrow drawn on it to show where North is located. If no arrow is drawn on the map, then the top of the map is North. In drawing your map, you should draw a North arrow on the paper, using the compass.
2. Map Scale
   Every map is a picture drawing of an area of land. It is drawn to a certain scale or small measurement so the land distance can be drawn on the map.

   Map scales are usually in inches or fractions of inches for so many feet. Select a scale that will allow you to draw your field study area on the map paper. Be sure to draw the scale on your map. Map scale may be shown in two ways:

   a. Map Scale:

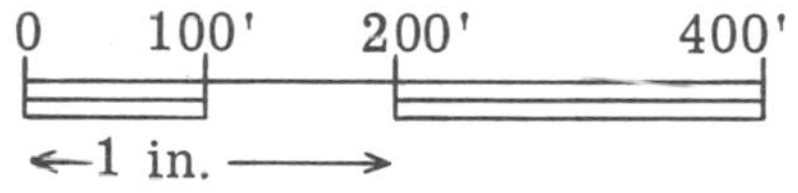

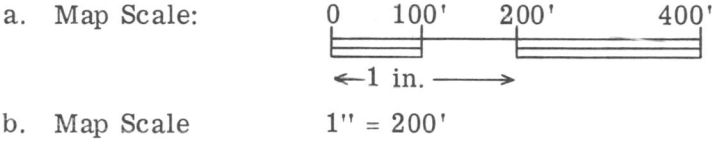

   b. Map Scale 1" = 200'

3. Map Legend
   On a map, the important details of the countryside are shown with special signs or symbols. These are explained in the map legend. Most map symbols look something like the actual thing they stand for. On the opposite page are some of the more common symbols you will need to make a sketch of your field study area.

E. DRAWING THE MAP

You have now completed taking and recording all the distances, compass bearings and land features on the Record of Field Survey form. Now you must draw your map from the field notes. These instructions will help you draw the map.

1. Select a map scale and convert the field survey distances to map inches. Draw the map scale on map paper.
2. Determine a North direction for your map and how you want to draw the map on the map paper. The lines on the map paper can serve as North-South guides.
3. Orient the map paper and compass to magnetic north by setting 360° or 0° over the direction of travel arrow line on your silva compass. Set the compass on the map paper with the direction of travel arrow pointing to the top of the map paper. Turn the map paper and compass together until the magnetic needle is centered over the orienting arrow in the housing. All three compass arrows should be pointing in the same direction. Your map paper and compass are now oriented to magnetic north. (DO NOT MOVE THE MAP PAPER!!)

LEGEND

Pond, or Lake
Intermittent Stream
Perennial Stream
Spring
Wet Spot
Marsh
Natural Barrier
Important Ridgetop
Deep Gully
Rock Outcrop
Unimproved Road
TRAIL
Trail
Deciduous Trees
Coniferous Trees
Boundary
X 1234
Elevation
678
Contour Line
MAP
Falls, or Rapids
Lava Flow
Shelter Beds
Sand Dunes
Fence
Road Bridge
Foot Bridge
Power Lines
Telephone Lines
Improved Road
Dry Lake
Mountain or Peak
District Guard Station
Guard Station
SYMBOLS

4. Remove the compass and turn the compass dial until the first degree reading on the field notes is over the direction of travel arrow.
5. Make a dot on the map paper to indicate your starting point. You may have to determine the location by experimenting to be certain that the map of the field study area will fit onto the map paper.
6. Hold a pencil on the starting dot and place one side of the plastic base of your compass against the pencil. Move the compass around the pencil until the orienting arrow and the magnetic needle are both pointing in the same direction. (DO NOT MOVE THE MAP PAPER!!)
7. Draw a straight line on the map in the direction of the direction of travel arrow, using the compass as a guide. Make a dot on the line you drew to indicate the map distance (the actual distance you measured on the ground).
8. Draw in the landmarks from your field notes on the map at correct distances along the line.
9. Now remove the compass and turn compass dial until the degree reading for the second distance is over the direction of travel arrow, as in instruction 4.
10. Hold pencil on the dot at the end of the first line and place one side of the plastic base of your compass against the pencil. Rotate compass as in instruction 6. Draw a line as shown by the direction of travel arrow to the distance you traveled on the second degree reading.
11. Add landmarks from your field notes as in instruction 8. Continue drawing the field study notes on your map in this manner until your map sketch is complete.

DRAW MAP OF FIELD STUDY AREA:

F. WATERSHED MAP OF AREA

All land drains water into streams, rivers and then into lakes or oceans. Each area of land that drains water into a stream is in a watershed named for the stream. All of the land that lets water drain into streams that flow into the Columbia River is in the Columbia River watershed. All of the land that drains water into the stream on your field study area is in the watershed of the name of your stream.

Instructions: Draw or trace a map of the watershed you are in and put in the features, such as streams, ridges, towns, your location, etc. Locate your field study area on the map.

NAME OF WATERSHED ________________

How many square miles in the watershed? ______________________________

How many towns in the watershed? ______________ People? ______________

List some of the land uses in the watershed. ______________________________

____

____

A STUDY OF SOIL

GENERAL INFORMATION

A. STUDY OF ROCKS
  1. Field Study
    a. List examples of rocks
    b. Identify landmarks
  2. Conclusions

B. STUDY OF A SOIL PROFILE
  1. Field Study
    a. Instruction for collection and recording soil information
      (1) Measure and mark horizons
      (2) Determine color
      (3) Determine texture
      (4) Determine structure
      (5) Determine pH
      (6) Determine temperature
    b. Collecting the data about the soil profile
      (1) Information above the soil
      (2) Information about the soil
    c. Analyzing the soil data
      (1) Effects of soil depth
      (2) Effects of color
      (3) Effects of texture
      (4) Effects of structure
      (5) Effects of pH
      (6) Effects of temperature
  2. Conclusions

C. STUDY OF LIVING SOIL
  1. Field Study
  2. Conclusions

D. STUDY OF EROSION
  1. Field Study
  2. Conclusions

E. LAND CAPABILITY CLASSES

F. HOW DOES SOIL AFFECT

G. A LIST OF SOIL WORDS

H. SUGGESTED SPECIAL INTEREST PROJECTS

I. INSTRUCTIONS FOR MAKING A SOIL MICROMONOLITH

J. DATA SHEETS FOR SPECIAL INTEREST PROJECTS

A STUDY OF SOIL

GENERAL INFORMATION

The story of soil formation begins with solid rock. For thousands, and often, millions of years, solid rock has been broken into smaller pieces by many kinds of processes. The freezing and thawing of water; pressure from growing roots; moving ice, water, and wind; and chemical reactions with the rock minerals all help to break up the rocks. Through the ages, these and other processes have formed the few inches of topsoil which support life.

Soils are formed from the bedrock and parent material. We can tell about a soil and what it is like if we know something of the rocks it came from. Rocks are in three classes according to how they are formed.

Igneous Rocks:

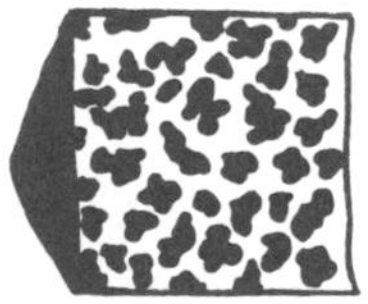

These are rocks which have cooled from molten masses, both from within the earth's crust and upon the surface. Many of these rocks came from volcanoes. Pumice, Obsidia granite, tuff and basalt are examples of igneous rocks.

Sedimentary Rocks:

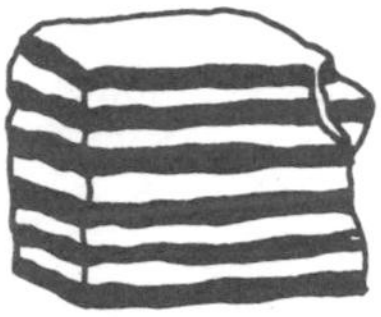

Some rocks are formed by deposited sediments from mud, chemical or organic residues. These deposits, when compressed into hard layers are called sedimentary rocks. Shale, sandstone, and conglomerate are examples of sedimentary rocks.

Metamorphic Rocks:

Some rocks are derived from other existing rocks. When rocks are affected by heat, pressure, or water to cause changes in their minerals or texture, they become new rocks. Examples of metamorphic rocks are: shale changed into slate; sandstone into quartzite; limestone into marble; conglomerate into schist; and soft coal into hard coal.

The darker topsoil (A Horizon) is built up gradually from the subsoil or parent material by the addition of humus from decaying plants and animals. Rain water washes fine particles and dissolved chemicals out of the topsoil and leaves them in the parent material below the topsoil to form

subsoil (B Horizon). These layers are usually lighter colored and contain less decayed plant material. They are more compact, feel smooth and sticky (clay texture) and air and water may not penetrate them as rapidly. In dry climates, they may contain many salty chemicals and become hard like concrete. Therefore, subsoils are not as favorable to the growth of plants as the topsoil. Between the lowest subsoil and the solid rock is a horizon of parent material that is mostly raw rock fragments and minerals that are poor for plant use.

Each soil has a profile or cross section that is made up of several layers called horizons. These horizons differ in depth, color, feel and chemical composition. Below is what a soil profile might look like.

As you look around the field study area, you may find soils that have different colors, some with more sand or clay than others, some with stones on the surface, etc. These differences can be caused by a variation in the kind of rocks and plants that have formed the soils. Topography, temperature, rainfall, and the age of the soil may also make it different from other soils.

If you dig below the surface of the ground, you may see how earthworms and other small animals help to grind up materials into finer particles as they eat their way through the soil.

SOIL PROFILE

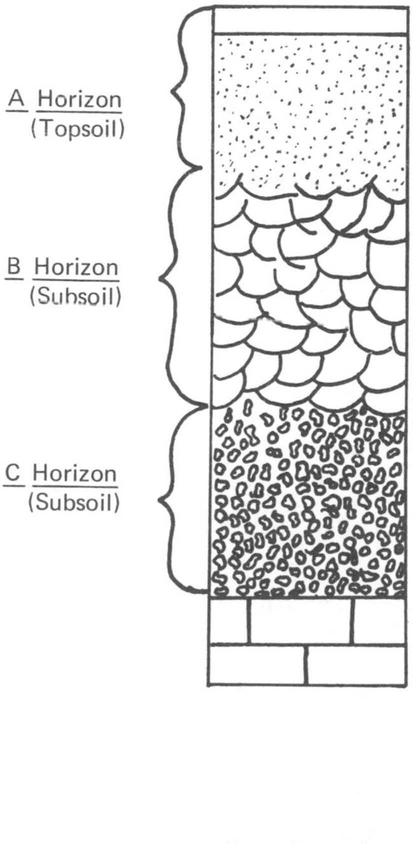

Duff	— Dead material on top of soil
Surface	— Dark brown colored - high organic matter, high biotic activity, abundant roots.
Subsurface	— Moderately dark - many roots, moderate biotic activity, moderate organic matter, commonly leached.
Subsoil	— Below plow depth - brown or reddish colored - more clay on the surface, fewer roots.
Lower subsoil	— More yellowish and less clay-fewer roots than subsoil, less aeration than above.
Parent material	— Unconsolidated - slightly weathered rocky or sandy mass from which soil develops, no biotic activity, few roots.
Bedrock	— Consolidated rock.

Date: __________ Time of Day ________

Weather: Clear - Cloudy - Rain

Warm or Cold: Temperature ______°F

A. STUDY OF ROCKS

1. Field Study

Collect and record the different kinds of rocks and rock layers.

a. List examples of the various kinds of rocks present in field study area.

KIND	GEOLOGIC AGE	LOCATION

b. Identify some of the landmarks found in your area, such as road cuts, stream banks, and gullies with exposed formations and materials.

LANDMARK	ORIGIN OF ROCK	GEOLOGIC AGE	CHANGES TAKING PLACE

2. Conclusions

Briefly describe the geology of the area in which your field study is located.

B. STUDY OF A SOIL PROFILE

Find an open soil bank or dig a soil pit on your field study area that you can study. Soil pit should be deep enough to expose the three horizons, if possible.

1. Field Study

a. Instructions for collecting and recording soil information in section 1b.

(1) Measure, mark and record the depth of each zone or horizon in your soil profile. Mark the horizons where they change color and looks.

(2) Determine and record color of each layer as follows:
Black or dull gray
Dark brown or reddish brown
Light brown or yellow
Light gray
Mottled

(3) Determine and record the texture. Texture is determined by feel and looks as follows:
Sand - feels gritty
Silt - feels smooth and slick, or flour-like
Clay - feels smooth, plastic and very sticky

(4) Determine and record the structure of the soil. When you pick up a hand-full of soil and carefully break it apart in your hand, it will look like one of the types below.

Platey

Columns

Blocky

Granular

(5) Determine and record the acidity or alkalinity of the soil. This is called the pH of the soil. Follow the instructions in your soil testing kit to determine the pH of your soil. (See page 4 - Special Equipment)

When you mix the chemical in your kit with the soil, it will change color. Match this color with the color chart in the kit and record the number beside it in the soil profile data.

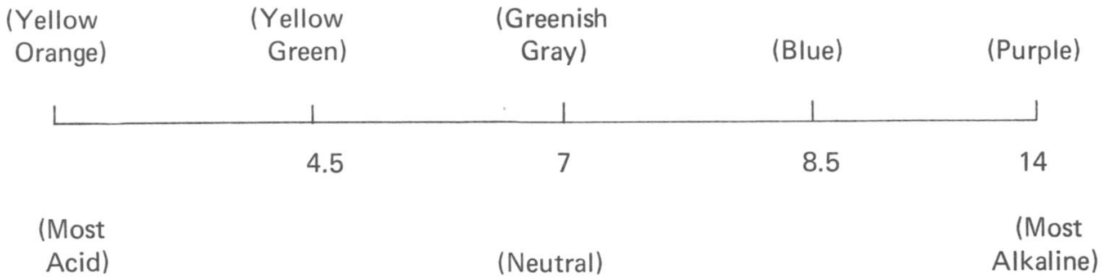

Some pH's of common items: Soap - pH-9; Seawater - pH8; pure water - pH7; sour milk - pH5; orange juice - pH4; Lemon juice - pH3.

(6) Determine and record the temperature of the soil horizons. Insert the thermometer into the middle of each horizon and leave several minutes or until temperature does not change. Use a thermometer that has a dial reading from 20° to 150°F.

b. Collecting the data about the soil profile. Follow the instructions in number 1. a and collect and record the following information:

(1) Information above the soil.

	In Open Area	Under Woody Plants
Air temperature 3 ft. above soil surface		
Air temperature just above soil surface		
Soil temperature at depth of 2 to 3 inches		

(2) Information about the soil profile: Sketch your soil profile, label the horizons and record the data.

PROFILE SKETCH

DATA

Contents of Duff: ______________________

__________ , Depth ______" to ______".

A. Horizon Topsoil : Depth ______" to ________", Color ___

Texture: Sand _____ Silt ________ , Clay ____

Structure: Colums ________ Blocky __________

Platey ______ Granules ___________ .

pH ______ Temp. ________°F, Plant Roots ______

B. Horizon Subsoil : Depth _______" to ______". Color ___

Texture: Sand _______ , Silt _____ , Clay ____

Structure: Columns _______ , Blocky _________ .

Platey ________, Granules ________ .

pH ______ , Temp. _______°F, Plant Roots ______

C. Horizon Parent Material : Depth ______" to "______", Color ___

Texture : Sand ________ , Silt _____ , Clay ____

Structure: Columns _______ , Blocky ________ ,

Platey ________, Granules ______ .

pH _______ , Temp. _________°F, Plant Roots ____

Type of rock in the bedrock: ________________

____

c. Analyzing the soil data.
The following information will help you interpret the data collected from your soil profile. This will help you answer the questions in Section 2.

(1) Effects of soil depth on plant growth and water storage.
Deep (42" and over) - Excellent plant growth and water storage.
Moderately deep (20" - 42") - good plant growth and water storage.
Shallow (20" and under) - poor plant growth and water storage.

(2) Effects of color on soil.

Soil Surface Color (A Horizon)	Amount of Organic Material	Erosion Factor	Aeration	Available Nitrogen	Fertility
Dark (dark grey, greyish) (brown to black)	Excellent	Low	Excellent	Excellent	Excellent
Moderately Dark (dark grey, dark brown) (to dark yellow-brown)	Good	Medium	Good	Good	Good
Light (Pale brown, yellow-) (brown to yellow)	Low	High	Low	Low	Low

Subsurface Soil Color (B Horizon)	Condition
Dull Grey (low rainfall soils)	Water-logged soils, poor aeration
Yellow, red-brown, black (forest soils)	Well drained soils
Mottled grey, brown or yellow (humid soils)	Somewhat poorly or poorly drained soils

(3) Effects of texture:

	Soil water holding capacity	Looseness
Sand	Poor	Good
Silt	Best	Good
Clay	High (low availability to plants)	Poor

(4) Effects of structure :

Type	Penetration of water	Drainage	Aeration
columns	good	good vertical	good
blocky	good	moderate	moderate
granular	good	best	best
platey (low rainfall soils)	moderate	moderate	moderate

(5) Effects of the pH on the soil: Plants need many food elements in order to grow well. These elements include nitrogen, phosphorus, potash and sulphur. The amount of pH affects how readily plants can get these elements.

1 — 4.5 — 6.5 — 7 — 8.5 — 14

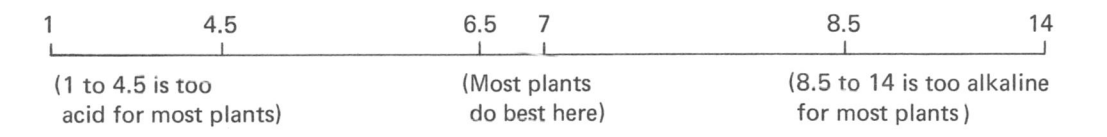

(1 to 4.5 is too acid for most plants) (Most plants do best here) (8.5 to 14 is too alkaline for most plants)

Example of plants in pH range:

pH 4.0 - 5.0: rhododendron, camellia, azelea, blueberry, fern
pH 5.0 - 6.0: pine, fir, holly, daphne, spruce, oak, birch, willow
pH 6.0 - 7.0: maple, mountain ash, pansy, aster, peach, carrot, lettuce
pH 7.0 - 8.0: beech, mock orange, asparagus

(6) Effects of temperature on plant growth: Plants do not grow well when the soils are too cold or hot during the growing season. The following chart of temperatures applies to most of the temperate zone.

Soil Temperature	Growing Conditions
Less than 40°F	No growth, soil bacteria and fungi not very active
40°F to 65°F	Some growth
65°F to 70°F	Fastest growth
70°F to 85°F	Some growth
Above 85°F	No growth

2. Conclusions about your soil profile:

Compare the data you collected with the information in section 1c. to answer the questions on the next page.

a. Does your soil have good water holding capacity? ____________
Why? ____

b. How does the texture and structure of the soil affect the movement of the water and air through the soil? ____________________
____

c. Does your soil have good fertility? __________ How can you tell? ____

d. How does the temperature change the deeper you go into the soil? ____
Will the air or soil temperature change fastest during the day?
____________________ Is the soil or the air the best insulator?
____

e. How does the pH change as you go down into the soil?
____
How does this affect the plants on your field study area?
____

f. How does the temperature differ in the open area from the wooded area? ____
Which area would be warmer in the winter? ____________________
In the summer? ____

C. STUDY OF LIVING SOIL

1. Field Study

Stake out a square foot area of ground on your field study plot and carefully inspect all of the soil in this area to a depth of 3 inches. Record all of the evidence of plants and animals you can observe.

Name of Animal	Number	Name of Plant	Number

2. Conclusions

a. What causes odors in the topsoil? ____________________

____

b. How do animals and fungus benefit the soil? ____________________

____

c. How do the rotting leaves help living plants? ____________________

____

D. STUDY OF EROSION

Scour erosion is a type of erosion caused by water running off the land. The slope of the land, type of soil and the number of plants growing on the soil all affect the amount of soil that will wash away.

Types of scour erosion include:

a. Sheet erosion - removal of soil without easy-to-see channels. (You can see this type on freshly plowed fields).
b. Rill erosion - many small, shallow, finger-like channels.
c. Gully erosion - deep ditches.

1. Field Study

Observe and record the slope of the land, types of scour erosion and the degree of erosion on your field study area.

a. Measure slope of land
   (1) Select the place where you plan to measure the slope and place a 50" stick on the ground.
   (2) Place a bottle half full of colored liquid on the 50" stick and raise or lower the free end until the water is level in the bottle.
   (3) Measure the distance of the raised end of the stick above the ground as shown in the drawing.
   (4) Record this distance in inches, multiply by 2 to determine the percent of slope.

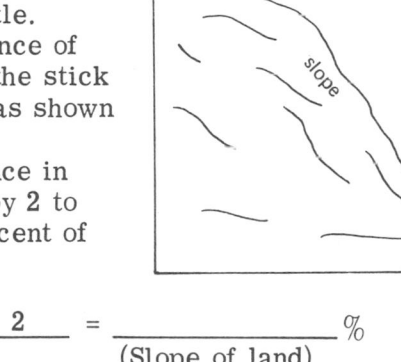

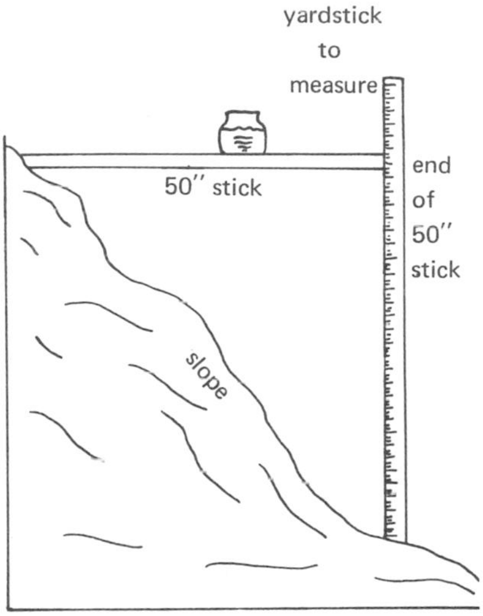

____________ x 2 = ____________ %

(No. of inches the end of the stick is above ground) (Slope of land)

b. Types of erosion present:

Kind of scour erosion	Check if present
Sheet	
Rill	
Gully	

c. Degree of erosion present:
Determine the erosion on the field study area and check the degree of erosion below.

	Check one
(1) None (undisturbed topsoil)	
(2) Moderate (small spots of subsoil show)	
(3) Severe (no topsoil left)	

2. Conclusions

a. Is the erosion natural or man-caused? ____________________

____

How can you tell? ____________________

____

b. What can be done to stop erosion on your area? ____________________

____

____

E. LAND CAPABILITY CLASSES

Land has physical features that we must evaluate to determine the best use of the land. Land has been classified into eight classes of use. Using the data you have collected in your soil study, determine from the chart on the following page what is the land capability class of your field study area.

LAND CAPABILITY CLASS CHART

This is a chart for soils in an area of one kind of land, climate and plants. An area with different kind of land, climate and plants may require a different chart.

Class	Slope	Erosion Hazard	Soil Depth	Drainage	Texture	Use and Management
I	0-3%	None	Deep	Well drained	Loam or silt loan	Cultivation - good soil management practices.
II	3-12%	Slight	Deep	Moderately well drained	Fine sandy loam or clay loam	Cultivation - few special conservation practices.
III	12-20%	Moderate	Moderately deep	Somewhat poorly	Sandy loam or silty clay	Cultivation - several special conservation practices.
IV	20-30%	Severe	Shallow	Poor	Sand or clay	Occasional cultivation - many special conservation practices.
V	0-2%	None to slight	Deep	Well to poor	Stony	Pasture, woodland, wildlife; machinery cannot be used.
VI	30-50%	Very severe	Deep to shallow	Well to poor	Sandy, silty or clayey	Pasture, woodland, wildlife; machinery cannot be used.
VII	50-90%	Extremely severe	Deep to shallow	Well to poor	Sandy, silty, clayey or stony	Pasture, woodland, wildlife; recreation, watershed; machinery cannot be used.
VIII	All	None to extremely severe	Deep to very shallow	Excessive to very poor	Rockland, dune sand, river wash	Wildlife, recreation, watershed.

The most limiting soil factor will determine the land capability class. For example: a soil with slope of 0-3%, erosion hazard none to slight, soil moderately deep, drainage poor, texture silty clay, would be Class IV, and could be used for occasional cultivation with many special conservation practices needed.

My field study area has ________% slope; ____________ erosion hazard; soil depth; and ____________ drainage; and ______________texture.

My field study area is Class __________ land and should be used for ________________

____

F. HOW DOES SOIL AFFECT:

Water? ____________________

Plants? ____________________

Wildlife? ____________________

Man? ____________________

G. A LIST OF SOIL WORDS

<u>Accelerated Erosion</u> - Man's misuse of land speeds up nature's process and results in excessive soil loss.

<u>Fertile</u> - Applied to soils, this means soil which contains all things essential for good plant growth.

<u>Geology</u> - The science dealing with the structure of the earth's crust; it includes the study of rock formations and early forms of animal life found as fossils in rocks.

<u>Geologic Erosion</u> - The never ending, slow process of nature in making soils and moving them about.

<u>Horizon</u> - A layer of soil material differing from other layers in properties such as depth, color, feel and chemical composition.

<u>Humus</u> - Decayed organic matter that stains and darkens the top layers of soil.

<u>Infiltration Rate</u> - The rate at which soil will take water.

<u>Inorganic</u> - Mineral, inert or non-life type of matter.

<u>Legumes</u> - Broad leaved vegetation which takes nitrogen from the air and stores it in its root system.

<u>Micromonolith</u> - A card with samples of the different layers, or layer, of soil glued on it.

<u>Organic</u> - Matter which has been related to life or life processes which is subject to decay by bacteria.

<u>pH</u> - The number designation of the amount of acid or alkalie in the soils.

<u>Reservoir</u> - A place where water is collected and stored for use. Usually related to a man-made structure, such as a reservoir behind a dam.

<u>Scour Erosion</u> - A type of erosion, wearing away of the land surface, caused by water running off the land.

<u>Soil</u> - Decayed rock or parent material and usually mixed with organic matter.

<u>Soil Profile</u> - A cross-section showing the "layers" of soil -- columnar. It affects the drainage and air and water intake of the soil.

<u>Tap Roots</u> - Roots which penetrate the soil downward rather than laterally.

<u>Texture</u> - The feel - sandy, loamy, clayey; affects the water holding capacity and workability of the soil.

H. SUGGESTED SPECIAL INTEREST PROJECTS

Geology Projects:

1. Make a collection of rocks, mount them on a board or in a tray, and label them with their correct names. The geologic age and locality where they were collected are important to put on the label, and the date when they were collected.
2. Take photographs or make sketches of exposed formations present in your field study area.

Soil Projects:

1. Collect and label soil micromonolith samples relating to their location on your study plot and the difference due to the slope aspect. See instructions on Page 34.
2. Test the pH of different soil samples collected on your field study area. Correlate with difference in plant growth on plot.
3. Find examples of plant roots cracking rocks. Describe in manual.
4. Find examples of water wearing away rocks. Describe in manual.
5. Collect soil samples taken from a wooded area and from the open. Compare the color, weight, looseness of texture when dry. Briefly describe results in manual.
6. Look for usable clay. If found, determine the probable origin and use the clay in modeling animals, molds for casting objects of nature, and for clay plaques with leaf or other designs.
7. Record in manual the possible uses for soil in your field study area.
8. Using water colors, paint a picture of your soil profile trying to match the colors and texture of each soil horizon.
9. Using a soft pencil, draw a pciture showing how animals living in the top 3 inches of the soil actually plow it.
10. Write a story describing the soil as the earth's brown drinking cup.

I. INSTRUCTIONS FOR MAKING A SOIL MICROMONOLITH

Equipment:

1. Blotting paper
2. Cardboard ($4\frac{1}{2}$" x 8")
3. Knife
4. Clear waterproof cement
5. Plastic spray
6. Metal soil cutter (approx. 1-1-$1\frac{1}{2}$" x 1" x 5/8"). (Spice can will work - cut out bottom)
7. 3/8" block of wood (cut wood to fit inside cutter, leaving $\frac{1}{4}$" space between top of block and cutting edge of cutter.

Procedure:

1. Place wood block in cutter.
2. Cut blotting paper the size of the wooden block so it will fit inside cutter.
3. Place blotting paper (cut in step 2) on the wooden block.
4. Cover entire blotting paper liberally with waterproof cement.
5. Cover same sized area on the card with cement.
6. Push cutter into soil (use side of a soil pit, road bank, or other soil bank).
7. Push knife into soil behind cutter and pry out. This keeps soil attached to blotter.
8. Trim loose soil away from the cutter, to approximately $\frac{1}{4}$" thickness.
9. Push the block, blotter, and soil upward through the cutter until blotter and soil are above the edge of the cutter.
10. Slide the soil sample and blotter off the wood block into cemented area of card.
11. Take samples until all soil layers in the profile have been cemented onto the card (generally three: topsoil, subsoil, parent material - others may be duff, rock, etc.).
12. Let the soil samples dry, and spray with plastic spray.
13. The thickness, pH, color, texture of each layer can then be written on the card beside each sample.

CUTTER

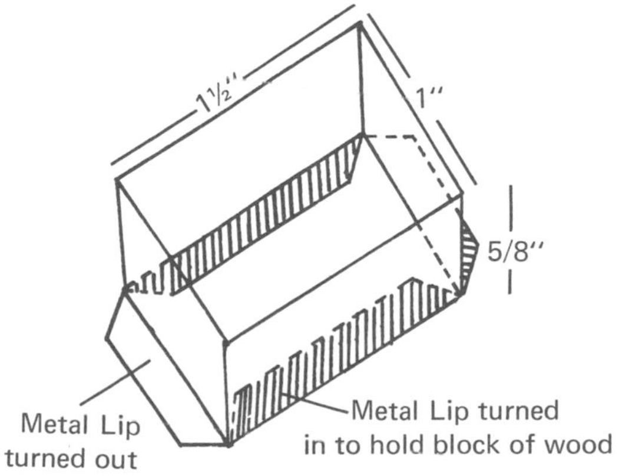

Note: The small plastic jelly containers used by restaurants to serve jelly make good soil holders.

CARD

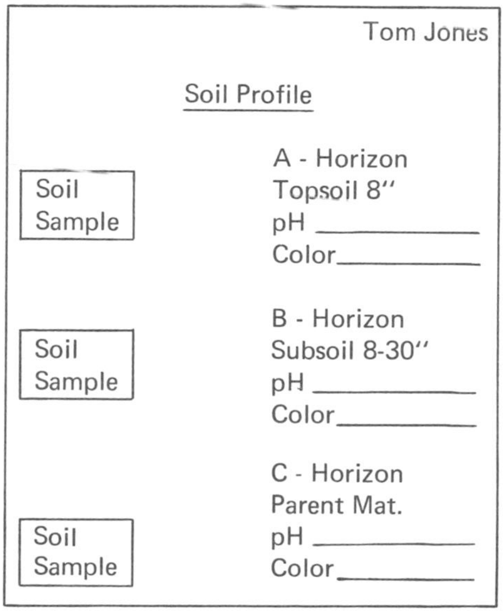

Date: ______________________

Time of Day: ______________________

Weather: ______________________

J. DATA SHEET FOR SPECIAL INTEREST PROJECTS

Description of Project:

Recorded Data, Observations and Conclusions:

Date: ____________________

Time of Day: ____________________

Weather: ____________________

DATA SHEET FOR SPECIAL INTEREST PROJECTS

Description of Project:

Recorded Data, Observations and Conclusions:

Date: ______________________

Time of Day: ______________________

Weather: ______________________

DATA SHEET FOR SPECIAL INTEREST PROJECTS

Description of Project:

Recorded Data, Observations and Conclusions:

A STUDY OF WATER

GENERAL INFORMATION

A. STUDY OF A STREAM SAMPLE
    1. Field Study
        a. Instructions for collecting and recording water information
            (1) Determine location of stream sample
            (2) Determine water and air temperature
            (3) Determine pH
            (4) Determine useable oxygen
        b. Collecting the data about the water sample
            (1) Sketch of water sample location
            (2) Location in watershed
            (3) Information about the water
        c. Analyzing the data
            (1) Effect of temperature on water life
            (2) Effect of pH on water life
            (3) Effect of useable oxygen on water animals
    2. Conclusions

B. STUDY OF THE AQUATIC ANIMALS
    1. Field Study
        a. Riffle examination
        b. Pool examination
    2. Conclusions

C. STUDY OF A STREAMFLOW
    1. Field Study
        a. Measure portion of stream
        b. Find how fast the stream is flowing
        c. Find the average width of the section of the stream
        d. Find the average depth of the section of the stream
        e. Find the cubic feet of water per second
    2. Conclusions

D. HOW DOES WATER AFFECT

E. AQUATIC INSECT KEY

F. A LIST OF WATER WORDS

G. SUGGESTED SPECIAL INTEREST PROJECTS

H. DATA SHEETS FOR SPECIAL INTEREST PROJECTS

A STUDY OF WATER

GENERAL INFORMATION

Water is our most valuable renewable resource. All life is dependent upon water for survival. Water is needed by man for industry, irrigation, recreation, etc. The freezing and thawing of water helps break rocks into smaller particles that eventually become soil. Water helps leach nutrients down into the soil so plant roots can use them. Water in the soil is used by plants to manufacture food and wildlife needs water in order to live.

Water renews itself through the water cycle. The elements that make up the weather (heat, pressure, wind and moisture) cause <u>precipitation</u>, <u>evaporation</u> and <u>condensation</u> in an endless cycle.

Because of heat, water in lakes and oceans evaporates and rises into the atmosphere. Here it cools and condenses, forming clouds which are blown by the wind. When the clouds contain too much moisture, it starts to rain. As the rain falls to the ground, some of it soaks into the ground and is stored in underground streams, caverns, or in air spaces between the soil particles. The underground streams form springs when they reach the surface of the earth.

The water that does not soak into the ground runs off into streams, lakes and into the oceans where some of it evaporates and returns to the air to form clouds again. Thus, the cycle repeats itself.

Some of the water that plants use is lost through the leaves by a process called <u>transpiration</u>. Transpiration in plants is like perspiration in people.

Label this picture of the water cycle, showing evaporation, transpiration, run-off, ground water and precipitation.

LABEL WATER CYCLE

Date: __________ Time of Day __________

Weather: Clear - Cloudy - Rain

Warm or Cold: Temperature _______ °F

A. STUDY OF A STREAM SAMPLE

Find an area along the stream in your field study area from which you can easily take samples of water.

1. Field Study

a. Instructions for collecting and recording water information: The following instructions will help you collect and record the water information on page 44:

(1) Determine the location of the stream sample in your area and its watershed. Do this by comparing the items in your streambed with the characteristics of a typical streambed in the chart below.

TYPICAL STREAM

Item	Headwaters of a Stream	Mid-region of stream	Lower Valley of stream
Slope of streambed	Steep, fast flowing	Gentle	Almost flat
Rocks in streambed	Large, boulders	Smaller rocks	Silt, sand
Temperature of water	Very cold	Cool	Warm
Amount of useable oxygen for fish	A lot of oxygen	Enough oxygen for animals	Oxygen is variable
Insects found	Mayfly, stonefly, helgrammite	Caddis fly, mayfly, stonefly	Beetles, worms, bugs, skaters, midge, larvae

(2) Determine and record the water and air temperature.

(a) Take water temperature with the bulb of the thermometer under the water.

(b) Take the air temperature 1 foot above the surface of of the water.

(c) Take and record water and air temperatures 3 different times during the day.

(3) Determine and record the acidity or alkalinity of the water. This is called the pH of the water. Use the same method and kit that you used in testing the soil.

(4) Determine and record the amount of useable oxygen in the water. Follow the instructions on the oxygen testing kit provided for you. (See page 4 - Special Equipment) The amount of available oxygen is called dissolved oxygen and is written as - so many parts of oxygen to every million parts of water - or ppm. (parts per million) Example: If the oxygen test showed 4, it would mean that there are 4 gallons of oxygen in one million gallons of water, or 4 ppm.

b. Collecting the data about the water sample.
Following the instructions in No. 1a, collect and record the following information:

(1) Sketch of water sample location.

(2) Location of area of the stream in its watershed. (Circle one) Headwaters Mid-region Lower Valley

(3) Information about the water

(1) Location of water sample (Edge or middle of stream)	Times Taken	(2) Temperature		(3) pH	(4) Useable Oxygen (ppm)
		Water	Air		
	AM				
Note: Take 3 samples	Noon				
from one location	PM				

c. Analyzing the data.
The following information will help you interpret the data collected from your stream sample. This will help you answer the questions on page 46.

(1) Effect of temperature on water life. Animals that live in the water have adapted to certain water temperature ranges. Below are examples of water animals you will find within these temperature ranges.

Temperature	Life Found
Greater than 65°F	Much plant life, catfish
Less than 65°F	Caddis fly, water beetles, striders, bass, carp, crappie, some fish diseases
	Best for trout, caddis fly, stonefly, mayfly

(2) Effect of pH on water life. Animals that live in the water cannot stand too much acid or alkali in the water. A few animals have adapted to acid or alkali conditions. A swamp is usually acid. A pond would probably be alkaline in summer, during plant growth, and slightly acid in fall during plant decomposition.

pH RANGES THAT SUPPORT AQUATIC ANIMAL AND PLANT LIFE

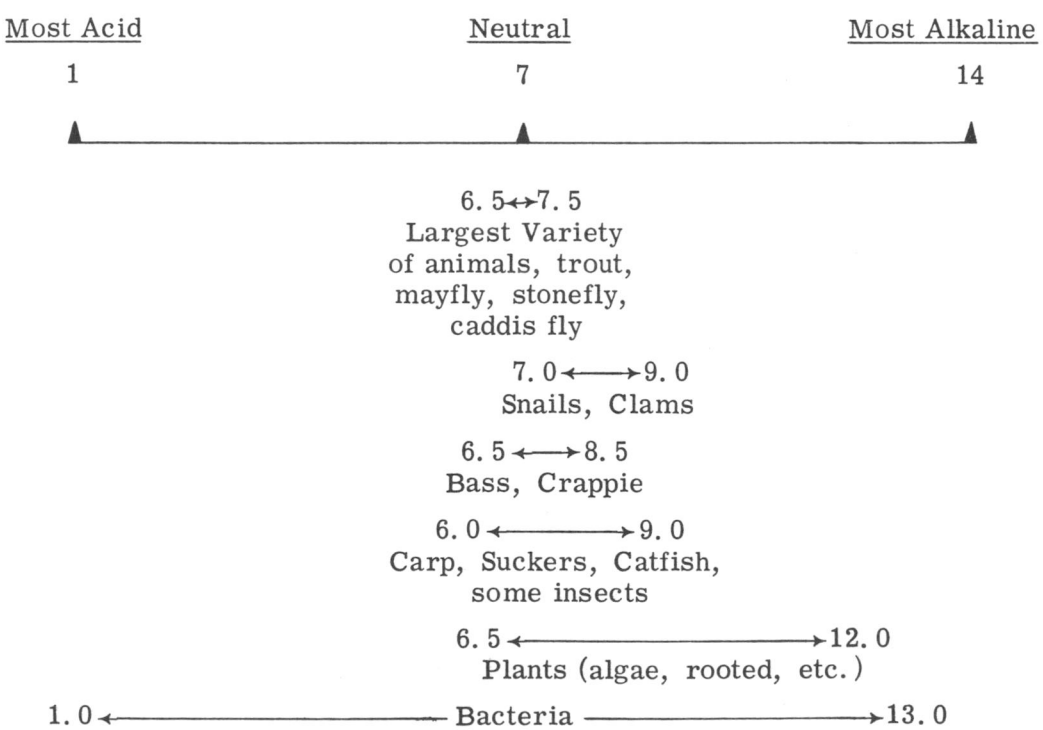

Most Acid — 1 | Neutral — 7 | Most Alkaline — 14

6.5 ↔ 7.5
Largest Variety of animals, trout, mayfly, stonefly, caddis fly

7.0 ↔ 9.0
Snails, Clams

6.5 ↔ 8.5
Bass, Crappie

6.0 ↔ 9.0
Carp, Suckers, Catfish, some insects

6.5 ↔ 12.0
Plants (algae, rooted, etc.)

1.0 ← Bacteria → 13.0

(3) Effect of useable oxygen in the water on water animals. All life needs oxygen to live. Pollution reduces the amount of oxygen in the water. Water plants also use oxygen in the water.

Lakes or ponds with large amounts of surface algae will fluctuate the most in amounts of dissolved oxygen during a 24 hour period.

During daylight all plants use carbon dioxide (CO_2) and give off oxygen (0) in the photosynthetic process. At night the reverse is true; since there is no light the process is stopped and the plant uses 0 and gives off CO_2. If a body of water has large amounts of plants, the available 0 in the water will be used at night by the plants and replaced by the CO_2 given off by the plants.

Useable oxygen in ppm reading	Variety of life
Below 5	Very little life can survive
Above 5	Large variety of life

2. Conclusions about the water sample.

Compare the data you collected with the information on page 44 to answer these questions.

a. Did the water temperature fluctuate more than the air temperature? ____________ Why? ______________________

____

b. Do water animals need as many seasonal adptations as land animals? ______________________________________

c. What animal life would you expect to find in this stream?

____

B. STUDY OF AQUATIC ANIMALS

1. Field Study

Collect and record the aquatic animals from a fast flowing (riffle) and a slow moving (pool) section of your stream.

a. Riffle examination
Examine the complete surface of the rocks for animal life present.
Place a collection screen or tea strainer in the riffle and shake the rocks and gravel upstream so the debris will collect in the screen. Now, hold it up so the water will drain out and the animals will remain in the screen.

b. Pool examination
Examine the muck, leaves and other debris in the bottom of the pool for animal life.

RECORD OF ANIMAL LIFE

Use the aquatic insect keys at the end of this chapter to help identify animals collected.

RIFFLE		POOL	
Kind	No.	Kind	No.

2. Conclusions

Is this the type of aquatic life you expected to find?

____

What fish would you expect to find in this section of the stream?

____

Is the water in the stream pure enough to drink?_______________

How can you tell?_______________

____

C. STUDY OF STREAMFLOW

Instructions for measuring streamflow:

1. Field Study

Instructions for collecting and recording streamflow measurements

a. Measure and mark with stakes a 100 foot distance along a straight section of your stream.
b. Find how fast the stream is flowing. Throw a stick (2 or 3 inches long) in the water above the upstream marker. Record the number of seconds it takes to float between the markers.

Record below. No. of seconds to float between stakes: ________ seconds. Now divide the 100 foot distance by the total seconds it took the stick to float between the stakes. This will tell you how many feet the stick floated each second.

100 ft. (distance) ÷ ______________ (total seconds) = __________________ ft. per sec. (number of feet stick floated each second)

c. Find the average width of the section of the stream. Measure the width of the stream at 3 places within the 100 foot area. Record the measurements below. Divide the total by 3 to get the average width of the stream.

First measurement ________ feet

Second measurement ________ feet

Third measurement ________ feet

Total ____________ feet ÷ 3 = ____________ ft. (average width)

d. Find the average depth of the section of the stream. Wade across the stream in a straight line. Measure the depth of the stream in 3 places along the straight line. Record measurements below. Divide the total by 3 to get the average depth of the stream.

First measurement ________ feet

Second measurement ________ feet

Third measurement ________ feet

Total ____________ feet ÷ 3 = ____________ ft. (average depth)

e. Find the cubic feet of water per second. Multiply the average depth and the number of feet the stick floated each second. This will tell you the number of cubic feet of water flowing in the stream every second.

________ (average width) x ________ (average depth) x __________ (number of feet per second) = __________________ (cubic ft. of water flowing per second)

Note: A cubic foot of water is the water in a container 1 foot wide, 1 foot high and 1 foot long .

2. Conclusions

Use this table of water measurements to answer the question below:

TABLE OF WATER MEASUREMENTS

A Water Flow of 1 Cubic Foot Per Second	=	448.83 Gallons Per Minute
One cubic foot of water	=	7.48 gallons
One cubic foot of water	=	62.4 pounds

a. How many gallons of water flow is in this stream every second?

______	x	7.48	=	______
(Stream flow in cu. ft. per sec.)		(gallons in 1 cu. ft. of water)		(gallons of water per second)

b. How many gallons of water flow is in this stream every minute?

______	x	60	=	______
(Gallons per second)		(Sec. in minute)		(gallons of water per minute)

c. Each person uses about 150 gallons of water a day. What is the total number of people who could live from the water in this stream?

______	x	______	=	______	÷	______	=	______
(Gallons of water per minute)		(No. minutes in a day)		(Total gallons water per day)		(Amount of water one person uses per day)		(Total no. people who could live from water in this stream)

D. HOW DOES WATER AFFECT:

Soil? ______________________________

____

____

Plants? ______________________________

____

____

Wildlife? ______________________________

____

____

Man? ______________________________

____

____

SUB-SURFACE FRESH WATER ORGANISMS

1. Planaria *(Turbellaria)*

Planarians are fairly common in ponds, lakes, springs, and other fresh waters among vegetation, beneath stones, or crawling over the bottom. These free-living flatworms are usually arrow-shaped and vary in color from white to black depending on species and environment. Small planaria look much the same as the adult, differing only in size.

2. Bryozoan Colony *(Bryozoa)*.

Fresh-water Bryozoa are very common in lakes, ponds, and rivers. They are community dwellers, living in jelly type substance which is formed on sticks as a gelatinous ball or a mossy mat over the surface of underwater objects. There is a wide range in color, some colonies are brownish and still others have a greenish tinge. Colonies are made up of thousands of these tiny animals.

3. Leech *(Hirudinea)*

Leeches make homes in lakes, ponds, or other fresh-water areas. They can be seen moving about underwater by their well-known "Measuring Worm" type of travel, or swimming freely. Leeches are predatory or parasitic segmented worms with sucking discs which are used in attachment, movement, and feeding. They are usually dark brown to black in coloration.

4. Daphnia *(Cladocera)*

Daphnia are found in all sorts of fresh waters. The shallow, weedy backwaters of a lake whose water level is fairly permanent harbors greater numbers that any other kind of locality. These little crustaceans are virtually transparent and are best recognized by their two-branched antennae, robust bodies, and sharp-tail spine.

5. Cyclops *(Copepoda)*

These little fresh-water crustaceans are very familiar in all slow moving waters, especially shallow ponds. Their bodies, like the Daphnia, are very transparent and are characterized by the forked antenna and the branched tail. The female usually has two groups of eggs attached to her body just ahead of the tail.

6. Fairy Shrimps *(Anostraca)*

For the most part, fairy shrimps live in temporary pools and ponds of fresh water. They are frequently seen underwater, rowing themselves about on their backs, by means of numerous, similar, flattened appendages. These appendages are always faced toward the source of light.

7. Fresh-Water Shrimp *(Malacostraca)*

These are found in lakes, streams, and ponds in eastern and western Oregon. Shrimp are usually found among the aquatic plants, rocks, and algae. Usually they are nearly transparent and look something like a "sow bug".

SUB-SURFACE FRESH WATER ORGANISMS

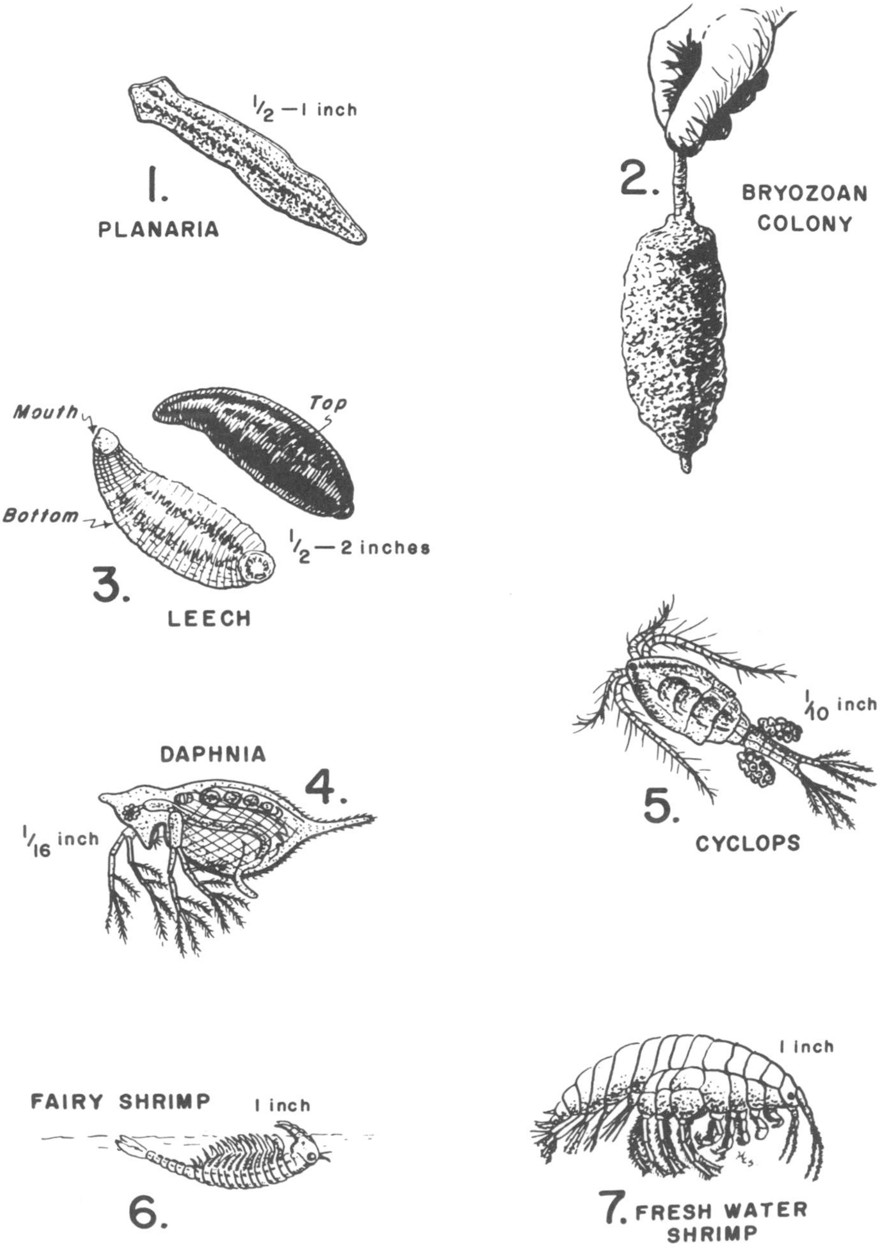

AQUATIC INSECTS

1. May Flies *(Ephemerotera)*

May flies are abundant in streams and lakes and can be found in practically all fresh water throughout the state. The nymphs are found on the undersides of rocks or other underwater objects. They have two or three tails. The wings of the adult are held in an upright position while resting.

2. Dragonfly *(Odonata)*

They are found in all types of fresh-water areas: ponds, lakes, streams, and swampy areas. The nymphs can be found crawling about on the bottom, on aquatic plants, or other underwater objects. They are one of the largest aquatic insects; most of them are dark brown to greenish as juveniles and change to brighter colors as adults. When resting, their four wings are held outstretched.

3. Stone Fly *(Plecoptera)*

Stone flies seem to require running water in which to live. They are never found in lakes except in the inlets and outlets. When the adult is resting its wings lie lengthwise upon the back. Nymphs are found in abundance only among the rocks in streams. Stone fly nymphs have two long and stiff tails.

4. Water Boatman *(Hemiptera)*

Boatmen are found in nearly all waters. They swim in an erratic pattern underwater and are usually found in slow moving waters. Boatmen are normally brownish in color and equipped with leathery wings.

5. Water Strider *(Hemiptera)*

Water striders are a familiar sight on the surface of slow moving waters, ponds, and lakes. They resemble long legged spiders. Although equipped with wings, they are rarely observed in flight. Their color is usually brown to gray. Many persons call them "water skippers".

6. Caddis Fly *(Trichoptera)*

Caddis flies are found in nearly all lakes, streams, and ponds. During their underwater life, they live in cases made from sticks and small particles of rock. These can usually be seen moving about on the bottom. When the adults are at rest the wings are held roof-like over the body and sloping down at the sides. The adults are generally dull brown or black in color. Sometimes the larvae are called "penny winkles" by fishermen. "Periwinkle" is another common name.

AQUATIC INSECTS

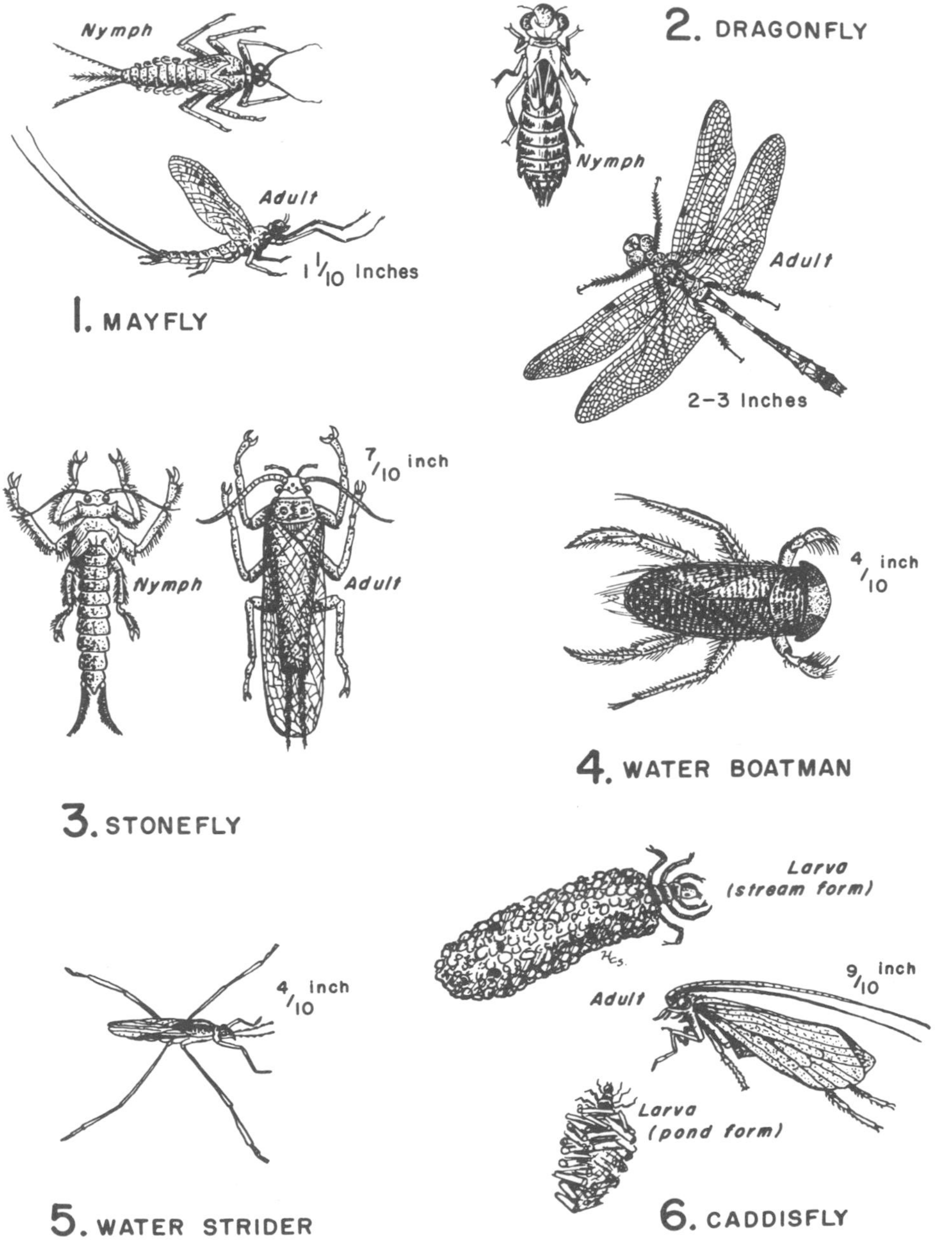
Nymph
Adult
1 1/10 Inches
1. MAYFLY
2. DRAGONFLY
Nymph
Adult
2–3 Inches
7/10 inch
Nymph
Adult
3. STONEFLY
4/10 inch
4. WATER BOATMAN
4/10 inch
5. WATER STRIDER
Larva (stream form)
9/10 inch
Adult
Larva (pond form)
6. CADDISFLY

AQUATIC INSECTS

7. Whirligig Beetle *(Coleoptera)*

These are found on the surface of slow moving waters, taking advantage of the surface tension. The Whirligig Beetles, true to their name, whirl or swim on the water's surface. When disturbed they frequently dive under the water. Their bodies are dark colored, robust, and the front legs are long and slender.

8. Crane Fly *(Diptera)*

The larvae of the Crane fly are found in scum of shallow waters, in the damp soil along streams or lake shores, and marshy areas. The adults are never truly aquatic and may be found great distances from water. The adults look much like giant mosquitoes without a beak.

9. Mosquitoes *(Diptera)*

Mosquitoe larvae are usually found in stagnant, slow moving water. Most people are familiar with the appearance of adults and know that they are more abundant around marshy, damp areas. The young are often called "wigglers" and can usually be found wiggling about just under the water's surface. Contrary to popular belief, not all mosquitoes bite; the males just buzz and are not equipped for biting.

10. Black Fly *(Diptera)*

The larvae are found in flowing water (only) on stones, vegetation, or other objects, usually in the swiftest part of the stream. In many cases, the larvae are so numerous they appear moss-like over the surface of the attached object. Later on in life, they live in a cocoon which is customarily a boot-shaped structure. The Black Fly as the name implies, is usually a dark compactly built fly, with rounded, short, black, broad wings. The adults may be found great distances from water.

11. Midges *(Diptera)*

Larvae are most abundant in the shallow water areas of lakes, ponds, and streams favored by a heavy growth of aquatic plants. They prefer soft mucky bottoms, as they are a bottom-dwelling species, and need this type environment for constructing their tube-like homes. Larvae live in soft tubes; however, during later stages of life they are found living in silken cocoons or gelatinous cases. The adult Midges look much the same as mosquitoes. Their antennaes look like two feathers on the front of their head and they don't have a beak.

AQUATIC INSECTS

7. WHIRLIGIG BEETLE

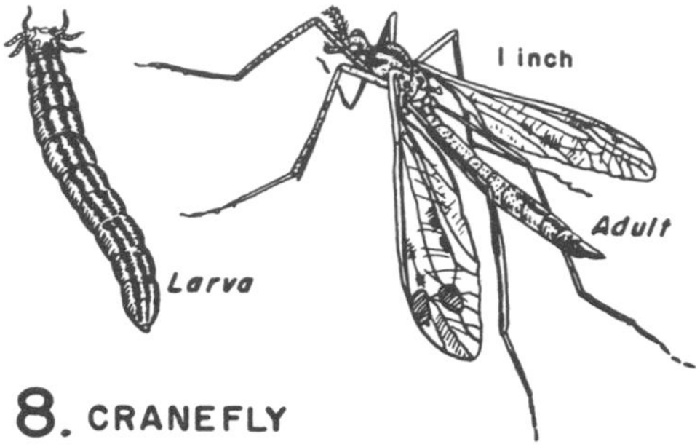

8. CRANEFLY

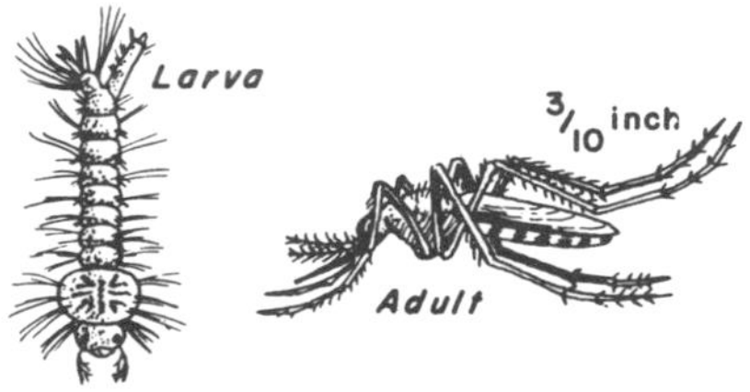

9. MOSQUITO

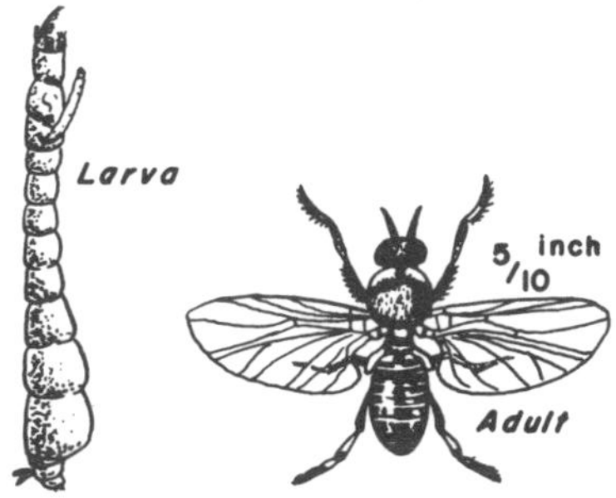

10. BLACK FLY

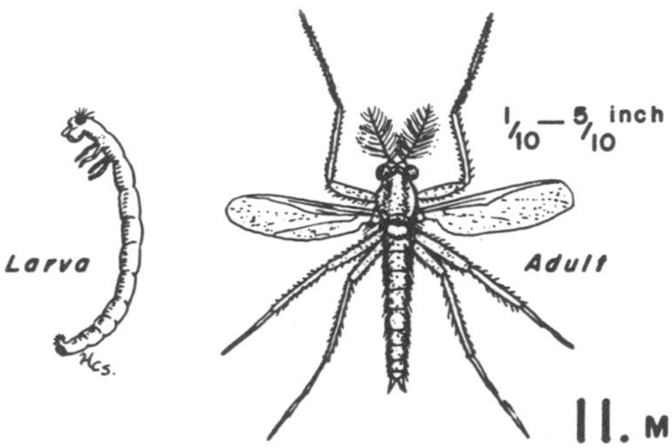

11. MIDGE

F. A LIST OF WATER WORDS

Distribution - A problem of water when demands exceed supply in one part of a region, although there may be a surplus in in other parts of the region or adjacent regions.

Dissolved Oxygen - The useable oxygen dissolved in a stream, lake, ocean or other body of water. It is essential to fish and aquatic life. There must be at least four parts of useable oxygen for every one million parts of water for aquatic life to live.

Evaporation - The turning of water into vapor. Water changing from liquid to gas.

Free Water - Surplus water which occurs when not used by plant life.

Pollution - Discharge of wastes which causes unreasonable and adverse effects to other beneficial water uses.

Pool - A deep, still spot in a river.

ppm - Parts per million

Precipitation - Cold particles that unite and form drops of water, which fall to the earth as rain, or freeze in the form of snow, hail, or sleet.

Riffle - A rocky obstruction in a stream that produces a ripple or a stretch of shallow, rapid or choppy water.

Run-off - The water which flows off the land through surface streams.

Sediment - Any material carried in suspension in water which will settle out as the velocity of the water lessens.

Transpiration - The process by which plants dissipate water into the atmosphere from their leaves and other surfaces. This loss is by evaporation. This is sometimes termed evapotranspiration.

Wastes - Domestic sewage, waters from industrial processes, return irrigation waters, and/or any other waters which have been used by man and altered in the process.

Watershed - A natural basin or area where water is naturally stored for later distribution through a river or stream or ground-water system. Any area of land which drains into a particular stream or other body of water.

Water Quality - A term to describe the chemical, physical, biological and radiological characteristics of water in respect to the suitability for a particular purpose.

Water Supply - That water which is naturally delivered to us by the natural water cycle.

Water Table - The height at which free water occurs in the soil profile.

G. SUGGESTED SPECIAL INTEREST PROJECTS

1. Observe how vegetation may affect the rate at which water moves in the ground. Record observations.
2. Follow along a small stream to its source and see where it originates. Record observations.
3. Observe a beaver dam to see how beaver activities can alter the water supply. Record observations.
4. Study how to improve the quality of water in a stream, lake or pond site. Record findings in manual.
5. Observe transpiration of plants by coating both sides of the leaves with vasoline. Record observations.
6. Measure the water flow in a fast flowing and slow flowing portion of your stream. Collect and record the temperature, stream flow, pH, dissolved oxygen, condition of streambank. Discuss similarities and differences and their effect upon the type of animal life you would expect to find.
7. Describe your thoughts about the appearance of dewdrops of water on a leaf early in the morning by composing a poem.
8. Write a story about the life-giving qualities of water.
9. Observe and record the differences between the shape and sizes of the insect larvae found in the riffle and pool portions of your stream.
10. Collect some algae from the stream and observe under the microscope the different forms of plant and animal life associated with it.

Dates: ______________________

Time of Day: ______________________

Weather: ______________________

H. DATA SHEET FOR SPECIAL INTEREST PROJECTS

Description of Project:

Recorded data, observations and conclusions:

Dates: ______________________

Time of Day: ______________________

Weather: ______________________

DATA SHEET FOR SPECIAL INTEREST PROJECTS

Description of Project:

Recorded data, observations and conclusions:

Dates: ____________________

Time of Day: ____________________

Weather: ____________________

DATA SHEET FOR SPECIAL INTEREST PROJECTS

Description of Projects:

Recorded data, observations and conclusions:

A STUDY OF PLANTS

GENERAL INFORMATION

A. STUDY OF PLANTS LIVING IN A PLANT COMMUNITY
   1. Field Study
   2. Conclusions

B. STUDY OF FOREST INFLUENCES
   1. Field Study
   2. Conclusions

C. STUDY OF TREE AGES
   1. Field Study
   2. Conclusions

D. STUDY OF PLANT COMPETITION
   1. Field Study
   2. Conclusions

E. STUDY OF A ROTTEN LOG
   1. Field Study
   2. Conclusions

F. STUDY OF A SINGLE TREE
   1. Field Study
   2. Conclusions

G. HOW DO PLANTS AFFECT

H. A LIST OF PLANT WORDS

I. SUGGESTED SPECIAL INTEREST PROJECTS

J. DATA SHEETS FOR SPECIAL INTEREST PROJECTS

A STUDY OF PLANTS

GENERAL INFORMATION

Plants are living things. They grow from seed to maturity, reach old age, and finally die. They take water and nutrients from the soil, combine it with the sun's rays, and manufacture food in their leaves.

Plants live in communities and compete for survival and growing room. Plants have certain requirements for life and by knowing some of these requirements, we can determine where they grow best and how to manage them.

Plants that must have direct sunlight to survive are called shade <u>intolerant</u>. Plants that can survive in the shade are called shade <u>tolerant</u> plants. If a plant does not receive enough light, it will not be able to manufacture food and will die. Many branches of trees die because the leaves are too shaded.

The intolerant plants reach for the sunlight. As they grow, the soil beneath becomes shaded and rich with decayed organic matter, making it possible for tolerant plants to grow. Only the tolerant plants can reproduce in the shade and when the intolerant plants die, the tolerant plants are ready to take their place in the plant community. The changing of plants in a community is part of the ecological plant succession.

Many times fire, insects, disease and man interrupt the plant succession. These are natural influences that can be beneficial or harmful.

Date: ________ Time of Day __________

Weather: Clear - Cloudy - Rain

Warm or Cold: Temperature ______°F

A. STUDY OF PLANTS LIVING IN A PLANT COMMUNITY

Mature plants grow to different height levels in the community. In the upper level, you will find trees; in the middle level, shrubs, bushes and small trees; and in the lower level, the flowers, ferns, mosses, mushrooms, lichens and molds.

1. Field Study

Collect and identify several specimens of plants from the upper level, middle level, and lower level of the community on your field study area.

Plant Name or Kind	Abundance		Where Growing			Economic Importance To Man
	Many	Few	Open Sunlight	Partly Shade	Dense Shade	
Upper Level: (above 30 ft.)						
Middle Level: (3 to 30 ft.)						
Lower Level: (0 to 3 ft.)						

2. Conclusions

How do the plants in the upper level affect the plants in the lower level?

____

____

What animals would you expect to find in the different levels?

Upper level _______________________________________

Middle level _______________________________________

Lower level _______________________________________

B. STUDY OF FOREST INFLUENCES

There are many things in the forest that affect plants:

Insects - bore into the wood, lay eggs inside the bark and strangle the tree, eat leaves and some eat seeds.

Disease - causes wood to rot and decay.

Wind - blows tops out of trees, causing disease and insects to enter the tree; helps disperse seed.

Fire - burns trees and other plants, allows some tree seeds to germinate.

Animals - chew bark, eat young trees, transport seeds, eat other animals that harm trees.

Man - Marks trees with knives, throws garbage in the forest and is careless with fire, protects and manages trees.

1. Field Study

Observe and record evidences of forest influences in your area.

Influence	Evidence of Influence	Harmful or Beneficial

2. <u>Conclusions</u>

What would you do to reduce some of the harmful influences on your field study area? ______________________________

____

How are some of the influences beneficial to other plants on your area? ______________________________

____

C. STUDY OF TREE AGES

Foresters need to know how fast trees are growing and their age to determine how best to manage them. There are 3 ways to tell tree ages.

1. Count the rings of a stump to tell how old a tree was when it was cut.

_______ Stump rings + 5 years = ______ age

2. Count the rows, or whorls, of branches on young conifers. (Most conifers grow one whorl of branches a year).

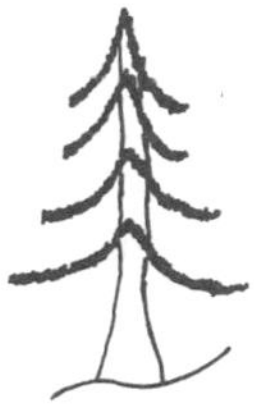

_________Whorls + 5 years = ________age

3. Use a tool called an increment borer to take a core out of a tree and count the growth rings on the core. (See page 4 - Special Equipment)

________Rings + 5 years = ________age

(Note: It takes about 5 years for a tree to become large enough to grow a ring of wood or add a whorl of branches a year. Add 5 years to each of your answers for total age.)

1. <u>Field Study</u>

Many times, you can reconstruct past events that have taken place on your field study area by recording the ages of trees.

Collect and record the following data from your field study area:
Tree Stumps: No. 1 - Age_____ probable species _____
No. 2 - Age_____ probable species _____
Standing Trees: (Count rows of branches on young conifers or use increment borer on larger trees).
No. 1 - Age_____ species _____
No. 2 - Age_____ species _____

2. Conclusions

Were the standing trees here before or after the trees were cut from the stumps? ________________ How can you tell? _____

____

____

If they were here before, why were they left? ______________

____

If they started growing after the other trees were cut, does their age help you determine how long ago the other trees were cut? ____ _____ If so, how long ago were they cut from the stump? ______

D. STUDY OF PLANT COMPETITION

All plants compete for sunlight, soil moisture and nutrients.

Enough growing space

Crowded growing space

Crowded branches and roots retard the plant's growth.

You can compare the ages and diameters of different trees to determine this competition.

1. Field Study

Follow these instructions and record the ages and diameters of several trees on your area.

a. Tree ages - Use one of the methods in Section C to determine the ages on your field study area.
b. Tree diameters - Take a cloth tape and measure circumference, or distance around the trees at $4\frac{1}{2}$ feet above the ground (D. B. H.) in inches and divide by 3. 14 to determine the diameter of trees.

(Note: The diameter of a tree in inches is about 1/3 the distance of the circumference in inches. Forester's have a diameter tape that measures the tree diameter. All trees are measured at $4\frac{1}{2}$ feet from the ground. This is called diameter at breast high, or DBH).

Measure and record the following data:

Species	Circumference at DBH	Diameter in inches	Age	Describe Condition of Tree
	inches ÷ 3.14″ =			
	inches ÷ 3.14″ =			
	inches ÷ 3.14″ =			
	inches ÷ 3.14″ =			

2. Conclusions

Is there a difference in diameters and ages of these trees?

____

If so, why? ______________________________

____

What would you do to release some of the crowded trees?

____

E. STUDY OF A ROTTEN LOG (A rotten stump can also be studied).

Rotten logs are an important part of a living community. They provide homes and food for animals and a place where certain plants can grow. The log eventually decays into the soil, changing its texture, color, depth, waterholding abilities and richness.

1. Field Study

Observe and record as many things as you can about a rotten log on your area.

BE SURE NOT TO TEAR THE LOG APART. IF YOU LIFT UP THE BARK, TO LOOK FOR LIVING THINGS, PUT THE BARK BACK IN PLACE.

Where is the stump of the tree? ______________________________

____

How did the tree die? ______________________________

____

What species of tree was it? (Look at bark, wood, structure).

____

List the living plants in or on the log.

Name	Location	Seed Source	Effect On Log

List evidence of animals in or on the log.

Name	Evidence	Food Eaten	Enemies

2. Conclusions

How does this log help new plants to grow in the community?

____

____

What effect do the animals have on the log? ________________

____

What will this log eventually become? ____________________

F. STUDY OF A SINGLE TREE

Find a tree on your field study area whose top can be seen from the ground.

1. Field Study

Observe and record the following data:

a. Type of tree (circle two of the following four terms)
   (1) Coniferous or broadleaf
   (2) Evergreen or deciduous

b. Species ____________________

c. Circle evidences of influences listed below and sketch what the influence looks like.

SKETCH INFLUENCE

insects

wind

wildlife

disease

man

fire

other

d. Record location of tree in plant community. (Circle one in each group)

   tallest or shortest
   crowded or open grown
   sunlight or shaded

e. List possible products of the tree ____________________

____

f. Age of tree; __________ years (your estimate)

   __________ years (actual age from one of three methods used before)

g. Diameter of tree; __________ inches (your estimate)

   __________ inches (actual measurement)

h. Merchantable height of tree.
   Merchantable height of a tree is that part of a tree from the ground up to the narrowest part that can be made into lumber. This is where it narrows down to 8" near the top. Estimate where the trunk narrows to 8" in diameter and then use the following instructions to find the height.

Instructions For Measuring Merchantable Height of Tree

(1) Choose a stick the same length as the distance from your hand to your eye with your arm/hand out straight in front of you, parallel with the ground.
(2) Now hold the stick upright to form a right angle.

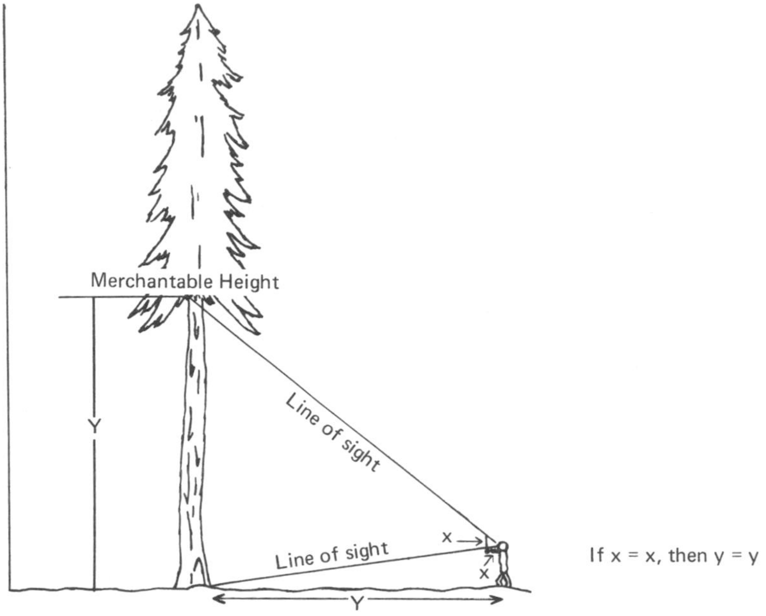

(3) Still holding the stick upright, walk backward from the tree, on level ground, sighting across the upper end of the stick.
(4) Continue to walk backward until the top of the stick over which you are sighting is at the spot on the tree you estimate to be 8" in diameter. Make sure your hand is in line with the base of the tree.
(5) You are now the same distance from the tree as the height of the tree that you measured. Measure by stepping off the distance.

________ x ________ = ________ Ft.
(No. of steps) (No. of feet in each of my steps) (Merchantable height of tree)

i. Number of sawlogs in the tree.
Trees are cut into logs in order to haul them to the sawmill.
Find out how many 16 foot sawlogs are in this tree.

________ ÷ 16 feet = ________
(Merchantable (height of tree) (No. of sawlogs)

j. Board feet volume in this tree.
When logs are sawed into boards, they are measured in board feet. A board foot is a board 12" wide, 12" long and 1" thick. Using the board foot volume table below, find out how many board feet are in the tree.

BOARD FOOT VOLUME TABLE

	Height of Merchantable Tree In Number of 16 Foot Logs							
Diameter In Inches	1	2	3	4	5	6	7	8
12	62	80	133	183	235	286		
14	64	88	147	210	274	338		
16	67	96	163	242	320	399		
18	71	109	190	280	370	459	550	701
20	75	123	221	330	435	543	651	758
22			2581	383	509	633	760	884
24				438	584	728	882	1035
26					666	832	1013	1190
28					750	941	1114	1346
30					850	1062	1291	1518
32						1195	1149	1700
34						1333	1614	1898
36	(Bd. ft. vol. table for second					1494	1782	2095
38	growth D.F. - Bul. 201 Table 13)						1955	2305
40	(U.S.D.A.)						2150	2523

To use: In the left hand column, labeled diameter in inches, find the tree diameter of the tree you measured. Find the column across the top with the number of logs in the tree you measured. Read the number on the table where the line from the diameter figure intersects the log column figure. This is the number of board feet in your tree. For example, if your tree was 26 inches in diameter and had 5 logs in it, it would have 666 board feet.

2. <u>Conclusions</u>

How many board feet are in the tree? ______________ Bd. Ft.

If there are 80 board feet in a picnic table, how many picnic tables can you build from the tree? ______________

Is this tree more valuable to be cut into lumber or to be left where it is for us to enjoy? ______________

Would it be more valuable for lumber if growing someplace else?

____

G. HOW DO PLANTS AFFECT:

Soil? ______________

Water? ______________

Other Plants? ______________

Wildlife? ______________

Man? ______________

H. A LIST OF PLANT WORDS

<u>Clearcutting</u> - A method of harvesting certain tree species such as Douglas fir in which all trees in a selected area are cut.

<u>Conifer</u> - A tree belonging to the order Coniferae; usually evergreen, with cones and needle-shaped leaves and producing wood known commercially as "softwood."

<u>Cones</u> - The seed-bearing body of such conifers as the pines, Douglas fir, spruces, hemlocks, etc.

<u>Duff</u> - Forest litter and other organic debris in various stages of decomposition, on top of mineral soil.

<u>Foot, board</u> - A unit of measurement represented by a board 1 foot long, 1 foot wide and 1 inch thick.

<u>Forestry</u> - The scientific management of forests for the continuous production of goods and services.

<u>Hardwood</u> - Generally, one of the botanical group of trees that have broad leaves, in contrast to the conifers; also, wood produced by such trees, regardless of texture.

<u>Heartwood</u> - The inner core of a woody stem, wholly composed of non-living cells and usually differentiated from the outer enveloping layer (sapwood) by its darker color.

<u>Increment, or growth</u> - Increase in diameter, basal area, height, volume, quality or value of individual trees, or stands, in relation to time.

<u>Intolerance</u> - The incapacity of a plant to develop and grow in the shade and in competition with other plants, such as Douglas fir and ponderosa pine.

<u>Multiple Use</u> - A concept of wildland management aimed at producing optimum amounts of available renewable natural resources from an area.

<u>Plant Succession</u> - The progressive development of a plant community, by replacing one plant community with another toward the highest ecological expression or climax.

<u>Pruning</u> - The removal of live or dead branches from standing trees. This may be done artificially or naturally. Natural pruning is the result of deficiency of light, decay, snow, ice, etc.

<u>Reforestation</u> - The natural or artificial restocking of an area with forest trees.

Ring, Annual - The growth layer of 1 year, as viewed on cross-section of a stem, branch or root.

Sapwood - Living wood, of pale color.

Selective Cut - Removal of individual trees from a stand of timber. Harvest of individual or small groups of trees over a period of years insures maintaining an uneven age stand such as ponderosa pine.

Slash - Branches, bark, tops, chunks, cull logs, uprooted stumps, and broken or uprooted trees left on the ground after logging.

Sustained Yield - Continuous production of wood at a more or less uniform annual rate, based on the yield of the forest.

Thinning - Cutting in an immature stand to increase its rate of of growth, to foster quality growth, to improve composition, to promote sanitation, to aid in better cover and to use material that would be lost otherwise.

Tolerance - The ability of a plant to develop and grow in the shade and in competition with other plants, such as western hemlock, western red cedar and white fir.

I. SUGGESTED SPECIAL INTEREST PROJECTS

1. Make a collection of plants, leaves, wood samples, seeds. Label and mount on cards.
2. Compare light meter readings under different types of plant covers and in the open meadow. Describe findings in manual. Relate to shade tolerant and shade intolerant plants.
3. Make plaster models of mushrooms.
4. Make a list in your manual of the different plants from the study area that are important in your everyday life.
5. Make a list of the edible plants that are growing in the area. Record in manual.
6. Make a woodland or bog terrarium representative of the different types of plants found on your field study area.
7. Take photographs of the different plants in the area.
8. Make a study of a moist or boggy location and a dry hillside. Compare tree species, soil conditions, and kinds of associated plants growing. Describe and record observations.
9. Make a study of the age and growth rate of trees in the area by using the increment borer. Mount cores on cards and identify type and age of tree.
10. Compose a poem about how neat trees are to sit under in the summer.
11. Write a story of how plants affect your everyday life.

Date: ______________________________

Time of Day: ______________________

Weather: __________________________

J. DATA SHEET FOR SPECIAL INTEREST PROJECTS

Description of Project:

Recorded Data, Observations & Conclusions:

Date: ______________________________

Time of Day: ________________________

Weather: ___________________________

DATA SHEET FOR SPECIAL INTEREST PROJECTS

Description of Projects:

Recorded Data, Observations & Conclusions:

Date: ____________________

Time of Day: ____________________

Weather: ____________________

DATA SHEET FOR SPECIAL INTEREST PROJECTS

Description of Project:

Recorded Data, Observations & Conclusions:

A STUDY OF ANIMAL LIFE

GENERAL INFORMATION

A. STUDY OF ANIMALS
    1. Field Study
        a. Invertebrates
        b. Vertebrates
    2. Conclusions
B. STUDY OF EVIDENCE OF ANIMALS
    1. Field Study
    2. Conclusions
C. STUDY OF HABITATS
    1. Field Study
        a. Habitats
        b. Changes in Habitats
    2. Conclusions
D. LIST OF BIRDS SEEN
E. HOW DO ANIMALS AFFECT
F. HOW DOES MAN AFFECT
G. A LIST OF ANIMAL WORDS
H. HOW TO MAKE A PLASTER CAST
I. SUGGESTED SPECIAL INTEREST PROJECTS
J. DATA SHEETS FOR SPECIAL INTEREST PROJECTS

A STUDY OF ANIMAL LIFE

GENERAL INFORMATION

All types of animals are born, grow to maturity, reach old age, and die. Animals live in a "home range" area. Animals are all dependent upon food, water, and shelter in order to live and survive. Food, water and shelter form the animals' habitat. If there are more animals than food, some animals will die. The land can feed so many animals and no more. This is called the "carrying capacity."

Some animals are tiny, some are medium size, and some are large. Animals such as the protozoans, worms, crayfish, insects, spiders, clams, and starfish have no backbones. They are called invertebrates. Others such as fish, frogs, snakes, birds and mammals have backbones and are called vertebrates.

There are many different kinds of animals in each study area. We will devote most of our attention to the wild animals which live here. Many of the smaller animals we will see in this outdoor laboratory live in tunnels or burrows underground. Some live mostly in hollow logs, stumps, or in shrubs and trees above ground. Animals which eat other animals are called predators. Many of the mammals, including humans, are predators. Those which eat meat are called carnivores, and those which feed only on plants are called herbivores. Animals that eat both meat and plants are called omnivores. Some animals, such as deer, elk, and pronghorned antelope are known as game animals because they provide hunting recreation.

Some animals are useful to man, providing him with meat, leather and furs. Others help to control destructive insects and small rodents. Mice, rats, chipmunks, and rabbits are important as food for larger mammals, such as the cougar, bobcat, coyote, and others.

FOOD PYRAMID

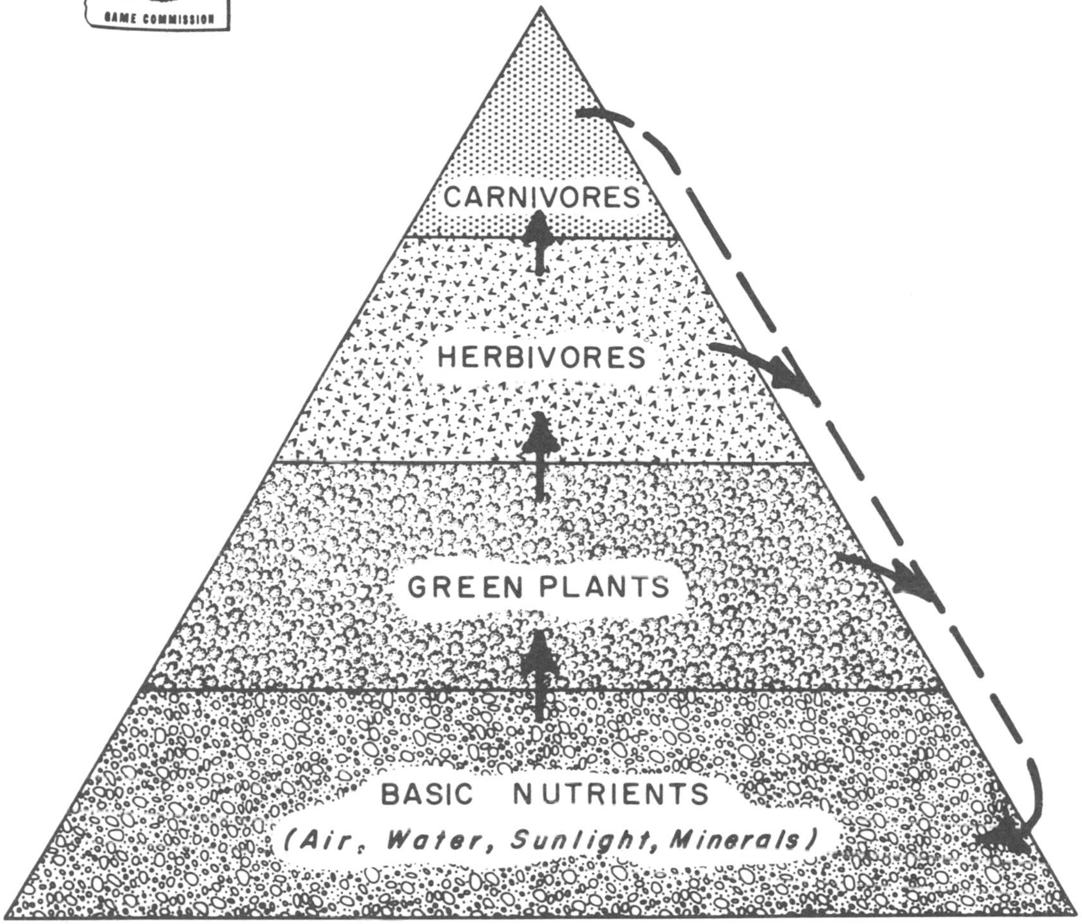

A DIAGRAM OF FOOD PYRAMID SHOWING GENERAL TRENDS IN FOOD CIRCULATION.

There always has to be a larger number of organisms below each level of life in the pyramid. For example:

> There must be more green plants than herbivores or they would run out of food; there must be more herbivores than carnivores or the carnivores would run out of food.

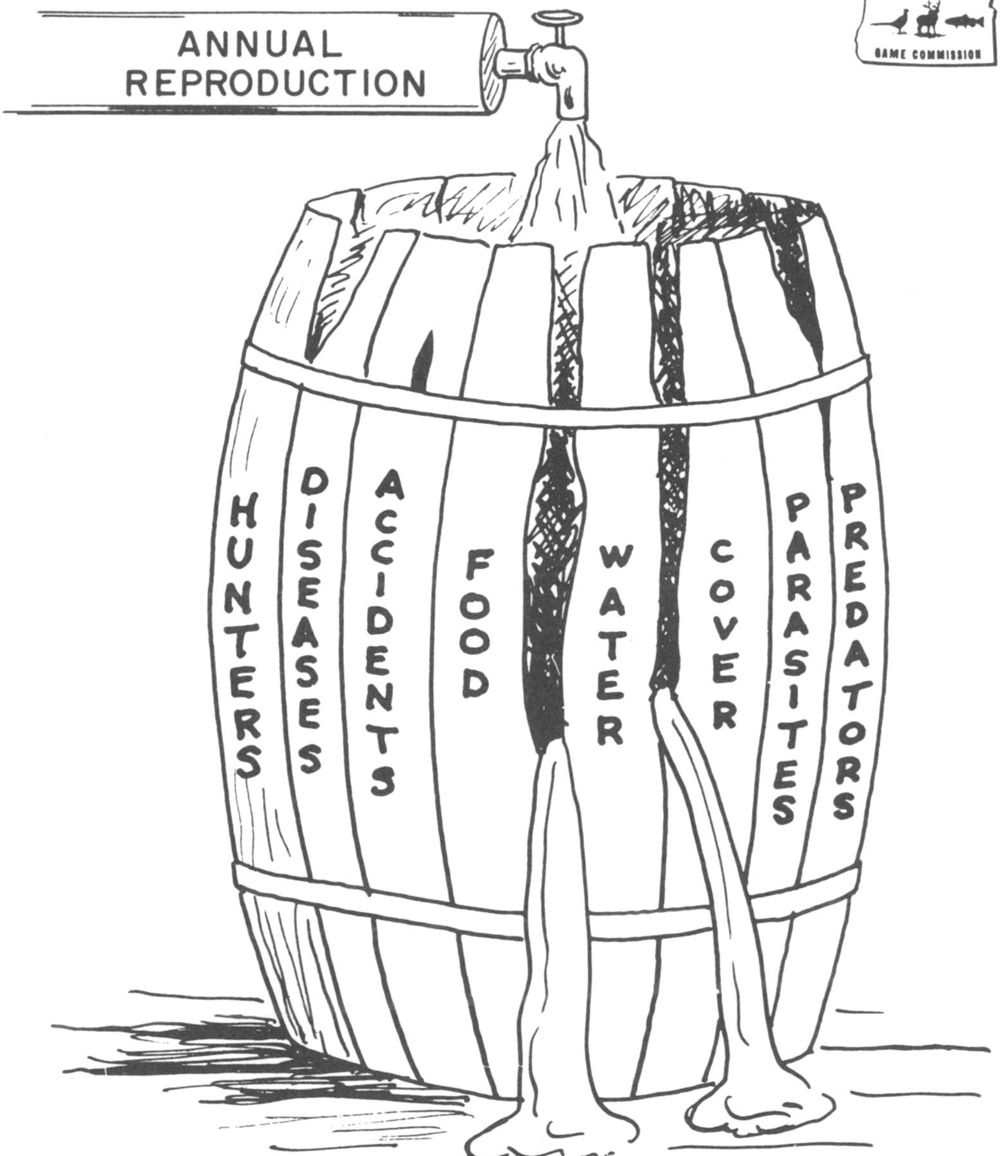

HABITAT BARREL

EVERY SPECIES IN THE WORLD HAS A TOTAL POPULATION WHICH VARIES FROM TIME TO TIME, AND THE HABITAT BARREL ILLUSTRATES SOME OF THE LIMITING FACTORS WHICH CAUSE THE POPULATION TO CHANGE.

Date: ______ Time of Day ____________

Weather: Clear - Cloudy - Rain

Warm or Cold: Temperature ______°F

A. STUDY OF ANIMALS

1. Field Study

a. Invertebrates:

Invertebrates are lower forms of animal life which do not have a backbone. Animals in this group would include the one-celled animals known as protozoa. Also included in this group are the sponges, jellyfish, flatworms, roundworms, bryozoa, snails, slugs, clams, earthworms, leeches, crayfish, centipedes, millipedes, spiders, insects, starfish and sea urchins.

Observe and record the kinds of invertebrates that live in your study area.

INVERTEBRATES

SIZE AND DESCRIPTION	KIND	FOOD PREFERENCES	VALUE

b. Vertebrates:

Vertebrates are the higher forms of animal life that do have backbones. These are the:

(1) amphibians
(2) reptiles
(3) fishes
(4) birds
(5) mammals

Observe and record the kinds of vertebrates that live in your study area.

VERTEBRATES

Size and Description	Group 1,2,3,4,5	Common Name	Type of Home	Food	Value

2. Conclusions

Did you observe more invertebrates than vertebrates? ____________

Why? ____

____

What predators did you find? ______________________________

____

Do they find their food on the field study area? ______________

B. STUDY OF EVIDENCE OF ANIMALS

1. Field Study

Observe, sketch and record any animal signs you can find on your field study area. Look for gnawings, tracks, droppings, dust baths, feathers, nests, runways, uneaten food.

ANIMAL SIGN	ANIMAL WHICH PROBABLY MADE IT	SKETCH OF SIGN

2. Conclusions

What type of signs were most evident? ______________________

____

Why? ______________________________

____

Were the signs made by resident animals or animals moving through the area? ______________________________

____

C. STUDY OF HABITATS

1. Field Study

Observe and record the different habitats in which wildlife could live on your field study area. (Streambanks, woods, rotten log, meadow, brush, etc.). List animals that might live there.

HABITAT	ANIMALS THAT COULD LIVE THERE

Observe and record the changes that have been made in the natural environment by influences such as wind, fire, man etc., which caused certain animals to move to other areas.

CHANGES IN HABITAT	INFLUENCE	ANIMAL THAT MOVED AWAY

2. Conclusions

What other animals would you expect to find in the area?

____

Why didn't you see them? ______________________________

____

What animals are found in your area that are not native but have been introduced and have adapted to this area? ______________________________

____

What would you do to improve the habitat for wildlife on your area?

____

____

For what wildlife? ______________________________

D. LIST OF BIRDS SEEN

Identifying Marks	Where Seen	Name of Bird

E. HOW DO ANIMALS AFFECT:

Soil? ______

Water? ______

Plants? ______

Other Animals? ______

Man? ______

F. HOW DOES MAN AFFECT:

Plants? ______

Soil? ______

Water? ______

Animals? ______

G. A LIST OF ANIMAL WORDS

<u>Amphibian</u> - Means "living in two places." These animals hatch from eggs which have been deposited in ponds or streams. They live in the water like fish when they are young. Gradually, they grow lungs and legs, breathe air, and live on land.

<u>Anadromous Fish</u> - Those fish which spend the greater share of their lives in salt water but migrate into fresh-water streams for reproduction.

<u>Aquatic</u> - Living or growing in water as a fresh-water environment.

<u>Browse</u> - The shrub plants which are food for wild or domestic animals.

<u>Carnivores</u> - Animals that eat meat.

<u>Carrying Capacity</u> - The maximum number of animals which a particular area of land is capable of supplying with food, water, and shelter.

<u>Environment</u> - All those factors which make up the surroundings of any living thing.

<u>Forage</u> - The grasses, weeds and browse plants which are food for wild or domestic animals.

<u>Forage Production</u> - The amount of food produced annually on an area and available for animal consumption.

<u>Furbearer</u> - Any mammal sought for its fur.

<u>Game Animal</u> - Commonly refers to those animals which are hunted for recreation and are protected by specified closed seasons or bag limits.

<u>Habitat</u> - The total environment which provides food, water, and shelter for wildlife.

<u>Herbivores</u> - Animals which feed only on plants.

<u>Hibernate</u> - To spend the winter months in an inactive condition.

<u>Insect</u> - A small invertebrate animal characterized in adult stage by having a division of the body into head, thorax, and abdomen; three pairs of legs; and, usually, two pairs of wings.

<u>Lake Survey</u> - A study of the lake to learn what physical conditions exist and what animal life is present.

<u>Migration</u> - Seasonal movement of animals.

<u>Omnivores</u> - Animals which feed on both plants and meat.

Population Inventory - A measure of the current number of a species of animal or bird. Since it is impossible to count total population, animals are observed on sample routes, and a population trend index is established.

Predator - Any animal which preys on other animals.

Protozoa - One-celled animals.

Range - The land upon which big game animals live. (Domestic animals may also live upon such land). i.e., winter range, summer range.

Reptiles - Like fish, are cold-blooded and their bodies are usually covered with protective scales or scale-like shells. This group includes snakes, lizards, turtles, alligators and crocodiles.

Signs - Something that indicates animal life is present in an area such as gnawings, tracks, droppings, dust baths, feathers, nests, runways and uneaten food.

Spider - Any of a number of small, eight-legged animals having a body composed of two divisions.

H. HOW TO MAKE A PLASTER CAST

The study of animal tracks is an interesting hobby. Much can be learned about animal habits by carefully examining the various tracks. To the expert woodsman and naturalist, tracks and other signs left by animals are like an open storybook which tells what has been happening in the lives of these wild creatures.

Here is how to preserve good tracks in mud or clay:

1. Clean track of loose particles of soil, twigs, leaves or other litter.
2. Spray track with shellac or plastic from pressurized can if available.
3. Form two-inch wide strip of cardboard or tin into a ring surrounding the track. Press firmly into ground to give support, but allow at least one inch to form edge of mold for plaster.
4. Mix about two cups of plaster of paris in a tin can or plastic bowl, adding water slowly until it is about as thick as heavy cream. Pour carefully into mold until plaster is about to top. Allow plaster to harden at least fifteen minutes before lifting out of track. If soil is damp, hardening may take longer.
5. When cast is hardened, lift cast out, remove ring, and clean the cast by scraping with a knife blade and washing.
6. Apply thin coating of vaseline to track and surface of cast. Place on flat surface and surround casting with a two-inch strip of cardboard or tin as before.
7. Mix plaster of Paris and pour into mold, making certain that top surface of casting is smooth and level with the mold. If you plan to use the casting as a wall plaque, place loop of wire in back of casting while plaster is still soft. Allow two hours for plaster to harden.
8. Carefully remove mold when plaster is dry. Separate the two layers and wipe excess vaseline from face of cast and track. Scrape any rough places with knife blade, or use fine sandpaper to smooth. Wash in running water.
9. When cast is thoroughly dry, paint inside of track with India ink or black poster paint. Label with name of track. A coat of clear shellac or clear plastic may be applied to protect and preserve the casting.

CASTING ANIMAL TRACKS

STEPS 1&2. Clean track and spray with shellac or plastic.

STEP 3. Encircle track with band of cardboard pressed into soil.

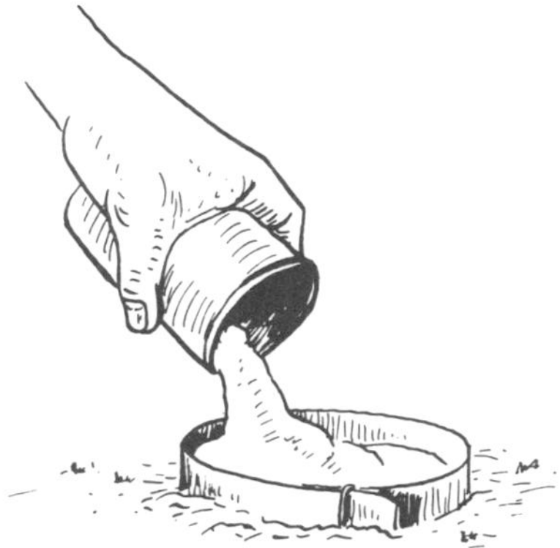

STEP 4. Pour plaster of Paris mixture over track.

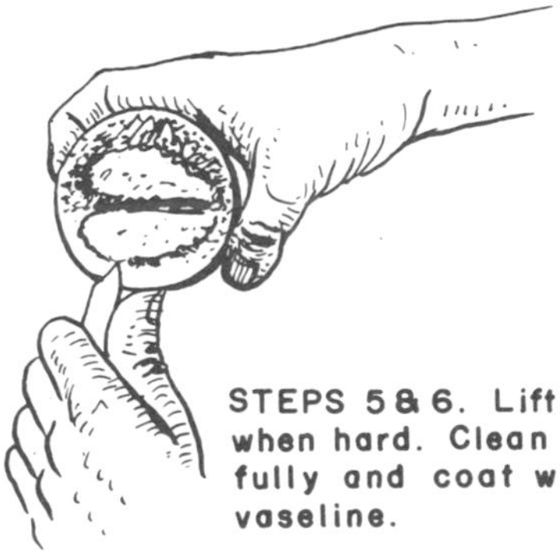

STEPS 5&6. Lift cast when hard. Clean carefully and coat with vaseline.

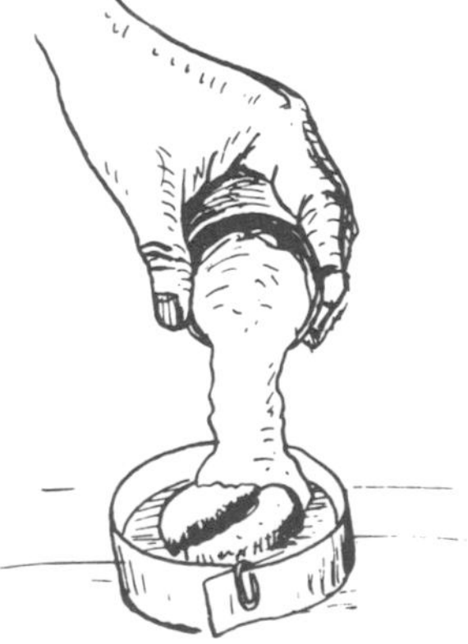

STEP 7. Surround casting with wide strip and pour plaster level with mold.

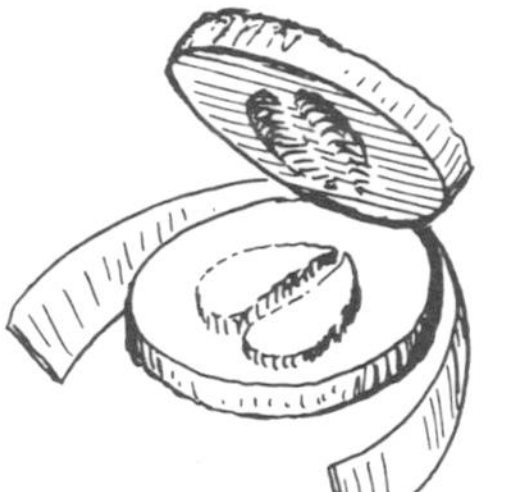

STEP 8. Separate the two layers of casting. Clean vaseline from track and smooth with knife blade.

STEP 9. When cast is dry paint inside of track with black India ink.

I. SUGGESTED SPECIAL INTEREST PROJECTS

1. Make a map showing what mammals live in the area and where they live.
2. Make plaster casts of animal tracks.
3. Take a photography hike into the woods and see what interesting shots you can take of wildlife in their natural habitat.
4. Visit several wildlife habitats to study differences in soil, plants, water resources and why animals and plants live there together. Record observations and sketch habitats in manual.
5. Collect, mount and label insects found.
6. Paint watercolor pictures of insect eggs present in area.
7. Find and make a spider web print. Write a brief description.
8. Find and observe an ant hill to see how ant activities affect other organisms and the soil. Record observations.
9. Find and sketch several birds' nests in their habitat.
10. Live trap small animals for observation. Record observations in your manual. BE SURE TO RETURN ANIMAL TO HOME RANGE AT THE END OF THE DAY! !

Date: ____________________

Time of Day: ____________________

Weather: ____________________

J. DATA SHEET FOR SPECIAL INTEREST PROJECTS

Description of Project

Recorded Data, Observations & Conclusions:

Date: ______________________

Time of Day: ______________________

Weather: ______________________

DATA SHEET FOR SPECIAL INTEREST PROJECTS

Description of Project:

Recorded Data, Observations & Conclusions:

Date: ______________________________

Time of Day: ________________________

Weather: ___________________________

DATA SHEET FOR SPECIAL INTEREST PROJECTS

Description of Project:

Recorded Data, Observations & Conclusions:

A STUDY OF WEATHER

GENERAL INFORMATION

A. WEATHER FORECASTING
   1. Rules and Tools
      a. Temperature
      b. Air pressure
      c. Rainfall
      d. Wind Speed
      e. Wind direction
      f. Clouds
      g. Relative Humidity
      h. Fuel moisture
   2. Predicting Forest Fire Danger
   3. Weather Proverbs
   4. Weather Flags

B. GENERAL WEATHER FORECAST INDICATOR CHARTS

C. DAILY WEATHER DATA AND FORECAST CHART

D. HOW DOES WEATHER AFFECT

E. A LIST OF WEATHER WORDS

F. SUGGESTED SPECIAL INTEREST PROJECTS

G. DATA SHEETS FOR SPECIAL INTEREST PROJECTS

A STUDY OF WEATHER

GENERAL INFORMATION

The weather is important to all of us. It helps us decide what clothes to wear, when to water the lawn, or where to go on picnics.

Weather is the condition of our atmosphere in relation to pressure, wind, heat and moisture. Heat mixes the atmosphere to make weather. Changes in the temperature usually bring changes in the weather.

Meteorologists use many instruments to forecast the weather, but abrupt changes can occur in the atmosphere and forecasts are not always accurate.

Each region has its own weather and weather patterns. Along the coast of Oregon and Washington, for example, rain storms usually come from the south and southwest, because of the southwest prevailing winds. In the summer, hot dry winds from the east dry out the forests and increase the forest fire danger. In the intermountain region of Idaho, Montana, Nevada and Utah thunderstorms bring lightning and the possibility of forest and range fires.

You should learn to forecast weather in your area from your own obsercations and check the weather a couple of times during the day to see if your forecast was correct. For example: If the grass was wet with dew in the morning, did it rain that day, or was it clear? If there was low fog that cleared by noon, was the upper sky clear or cloudy? If a southwest wind had been blowing the upper clouds for a couple of days, did they bring a rain storm? How soon after you saw a ring around the sun or moon did it rain? What does a cloud cap over a snow-capped mountain mean? What does an east wind bring in the summer? In the winter? These are some of the indicators that can help you forecast the weather.

Watch and record the television weather forecasts. Clip the daily newspaper weather predictions and check them against your weather observations.

In the study of weather, you will use some of the weatherman's instruments and your own observations to forecast the weather. Observe and record the weather items on the Weather Data & Forecast Chart. Make your prediction from the General Forecast Chart and Forest Fire Danger section.

A. WEATHER FORECASTING

1. Weather Rules and Tools

The weather rules listed are for the western parts of Oregon and Washington, but may apply elsewhere.

a. Temperature - The temperature affects the amount of moisture the air can hold before clouds form and they start to rain. Temperatures differ a great deal in the atmosphere. High clouds, for example, usually are made up of ice crystals instead of water droplets, so the temperature at that elevation is below freezing.

(1) Rules - Temperatures will usually rise if the wind is from the south or west in the winter and east in summer; or, if it is overcast during the day. It will usually decrease if winds are from the south, west, or northwest in summer and east in wintertime, or if the air pressure rises rapidly.

(2) Tools - Thermometers are used to record temperatures. To record temperature: mount your thermometer in a slotted or louvered box, away from the direct rays of the sun. Record the air temperature at about the same time each day, once in the morning, once in the afternoon.

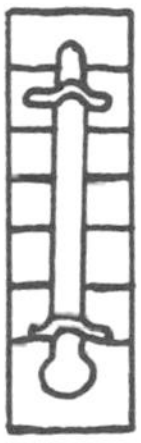

The Thermometer

b. Air Pressure - The unequal heating of the earth forms the pattern of air circulation. It also creates masses of air called high-pressure areas (or highs) and low-pressure areas (or lows). Highs usually mean fair weather; lows mean poor weather. The air pressure can help us determine the approach of the highs or lows.

(1) Rules - A rising air pressure tells of the warm air of a high pressure area and fair weather; falling air pressure, of a low pressure area and poor weather.

(2) Tools - Barometers are used to record air pressure. To use: locate your barometer where it is protected from the direct weather. Observe and record readings each time you take air temperature readings. (Note: barometric needle moves very little, so one or two tenths change in the reading is significant).

Barometer

c. Rainfall - It cannot rain unless there are clouds in the sky and clouds only rain when the ice crystals or water droplets reach a certain size, weight, and temperature.

(1) Rules - Rainfall is measured by the depth of water that would lie on the ground if none of the rain escaped. Rainfall, or precipitation, is reported by the amount of liquid which fell in a given length of time.

(2) Tools - Precipitation, or rainfall, is measured with a rain gauge. To use: place a rain gauge in the open, away from buildings and trees. Measure water in can with gauge stick. To measure the amount of precipitation in snow, invert your rain gauge and push it into the snow. Melt the snow by setting the can in a heated building. After it melts, use a ruler to measure the depth of the water in the can. On the average, about ten inches of fresh snow yield one inch of water.

The Rain Gauge

d. Wind Speed - When air is heated by contact with the earth, it expands, becomes lighter, and rises. It is replaced by colder air which, in turn, is warmed and the process is repeated. This movement of air causes winds.

(1) Rules - Wind speed indicates how fast the air is moving and in what direction. It will help determine how soon a change will occur.

(2) Tools

(a) This table will help determine the speed of the surface winds.

Observation	Description	M.P.H.
Smoke rises straight or drifts slowly	calm	0-3
Leaves rustle - twigs in motion	slight breeze	4-12
Small branches move - small trees sway	moderate breeze	12-20
Large branches sway	strong breeze	20-30
Whole trees in motion	moderate gale	30-40

(b) Anemometer - The wind speed can also be determined by the use of an anemometer. The anemometer is an instrument used when you want to know the exact wind speed in miles per hour. The anemometer consists of three or four cups mounted on arms that are free to spin. To use: place your anemometer atop a pole. As the anemometer spins in the wind, it

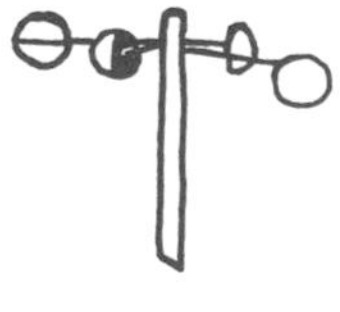

The Anemometer

makes a clicking sound. To determine the speed of the wind, count the clicks for a minute and read from a wind chart. By looking at the chart or using your observations and the above wind chart, you can determine the wind speed in miles per hour.

e. Wind Direction - The earth's rotation, temperature and topography all affect the direction of our air and help us determine from what direction changes in weather might come.

(1) Rules - Determine wind direction rules for your area. (See Chart on page 114) or Oregon and Washington.

(2) Tools - We can tell the direction of the surface winds by facing into them and using a compass to locate their direction. We can also use a weather vane.

(a) Weather Vane - A weather vane is a free swinging arrow on a pole and is made to always point to the direction from which the surface wind is coming. To use: before you can erect your weather vane, you must find the direction of true north. You can do this by using a compass. As soon as you find north, place a peg in the ground. Now, turn around and walk two paces and place another peg in the ground to show which direction is south. To complete your ground compass, place two additional pegs to form the east and west points. Erect your weather vane atop a pole, then place it in the center of the ground compass. You are now able to judge the direction the vane is pointing, using the compass points on the ground. Check your wind vane at the same time each day and record the direction of the wind.

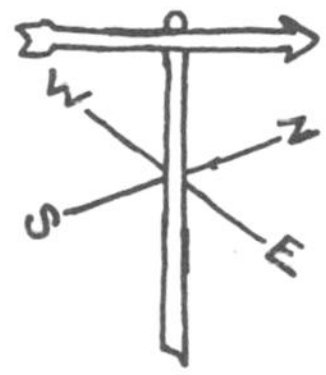

The Wind Vane

(b) We must also know the direction of the Upper Winds. We can determine this by observing which way the high clouds are moving. Stand looking up at the sky with your body and head against a building or tree with your body pointed north, or lay on the ground with your feet pointing north. Notice in which direction the upper clouds are moving.

f. Clouds - As warm air rises from the earth's surface, the water vapor in the air is cooled below the air saturation point and clouds are formed. The different clouds are indication of the type of weather we might expect in our forecast. See Cloud Chart for rules and tools. (See Chart on page 110)

g. Relative Humidity - Relative humidity is the amount of water vapor (in percent) that the air can hold at a given temperature compared with the amount it could hold before it rains. Air is said to be saturated when it is holding all the water vapor it can. When the air is saturated it is said to have 100 percent relative humidity.

(1) Rules - Warm air can hold more moisture or water vapor than cold air. As moist, warm air rises, it slowly cools until it eventually reaches a temperature at which the air is saturated. Further cooling forces some of the water vapor to condense out as droplets of water. Dewpoint is that temperature at which vapor changes to visible moisture such as fog, dew, or rain. If it is raining, the relative humidity is 100%. Low relative humidity usually means dry air and fair weather. High relative humidity means much moisture in the air and the presence of a low pressure area or approaching storm.

(2) Tools - Relative humidity is measured with a psychrometer. It consists of a dry and wet bulb thermometer placed side by side. The bulb of one is exposed directly to the air. The bulb of the other is covered with a layer of cloth that is dampened with water. The relative humidity is determined by the difference in temperature between the dry and the wet thermometer readings. The thermometer with the damp cloth will have a lower reading because evaporation of the water will make it cooler. To use: First moisten the cloth on the wet bulb thermometer. Now circulate air around both thermometers by whirling them in a circular motion. Keep whirling until each thermometer reaches a constant reading. Now take the reading from each thermometer. By using the table on page 111, you can determine the relative humidity.

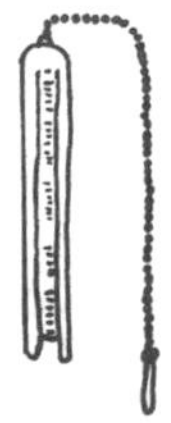

Psychrometer

h. Fuel Moisture - The amount of moisture in the dead material, such as limbs, needles, twigs, on the ground, affects how fast forest fires will spread.

(1) Rules - As the temperature of day air increases, the moisture in the air evaporates and the fuel moisture decreases.

(2) Tools - Fuel moisture is measured by weighing special sticks that have been exposed to the weather, on special scales that tell the percent of moisture in the forest fuel. If you do not have moisture sticks, feel the litter on the forest floor and determine if it is very dry or moist feeling. Break small twigs in two. If they snap when broken, the fuel moisture is probably low. If they break without a loud snap, it is probably medium or high. (Estimate if fuel moisture is low, medium or high in amount).

CLOUD CHART

(1) Rules Cloud Symbol	Name of Clouds	(2) Tools Indications
HIGH CLOUDS	These are the cirrus, or ice clouds, because they are composed of tiny ice crystals. Found at elevations of 20,000 to 40,000 feet.	
	Cirrus - thin, wispy, and feathery, and are sometimes called "Mares Tails."	Sky blue - fair Sky gray-blue "warm front"
	Cirrostratus - thin and patchy, and are rarely seen.	Fair weather
	Cirrocumulus - small, white flakes or globular masses that cause them to appear as ripples.	Fair weather
MIDDLE CLOUDS	These are the alto clouds that occur from 6,000 to 20,000 feet above the earth. These clouds can bring either fair weather or rain.	
	Altostratus - layers or sheets of gray or blue. They look slightly striped. The sun looks as if it is being seen through frosted glass.	Warm front Rain
	Altocumulus - patches or layers of puffy or roll-like clouds; whitish gray.	Possible weather change
LOW CLOUDS	These are the stratus or low clouds and they range from near the earth up to 6,500 feet. These are the rain clouds.	
	Stratus - low and like fog. Only a tiny drizzle can fall from these clouds.	Fine drizzle
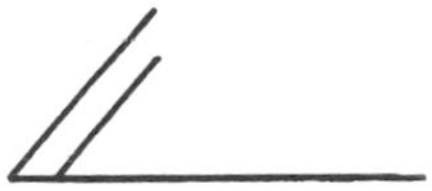	Nimbostratus - true rain clouds. They have a wet look and often there are streaks of rain extending to the ground	Rain
	Stratocumulus - odd shaped masses spreading out in a rolling or puffy layer. Gray with darker shadings.	Won't produce Rain
TOWERING CLOUDS	These clouds form at almost any altitude.	
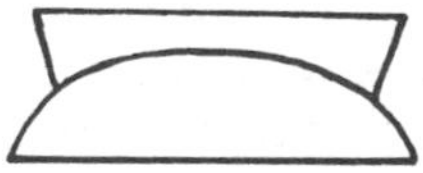	Cumulo nimbus - are the thunderheads; great air turbulence, very tall, almost touch the ground. Lightning.	"Thunderstorm" cloud; cloud-bursts of rain
	Cumulus - puffy and cauliflower-like. The shapes constantly change.	Fair weather cloud

RELATIVE HUMIDITY TABLE

TEMPERATURE OF AIR, DRY BULB THEROMETER, FAHRENHEIT

Difference between Wet-Bulb and Dry-Bulb Readings	-10°	0°	10°	20°	30°	40°	50°	60°	70°	80°	90°	100°
1	55	71	80	86	90	92	93	94	95	96	96	97
2	10	42	60	72	79	84	87	89	90	92	92	93
3		13	41	58	68	76	80	84	86	87	88	90
4			21	44	58	68	74	78	81	83	85	86
6				16	38	52	61	68	72	75	78	80
8					18	37	49	58	64	68	71	74
10						22	37	48	55	61	65	68
12							26	39	48	54	59	62
14							16	30	40	47	53	57
16							5	21	33	41	47	51
18								13	26	35	41	47
20								5	19	29	36	42
22									12	23	32	37
25									6	18	26	33

Example of how to use:

If the dry-bulb reading is 68° and the wet-bulb thermometer reads 56°, you determine the relative humidity by subtracting 56 ° from 68° and find the difference in the left-hand column. In this case, it is 12°. Run along the row of numbers opposite 12 until you are beneath the nearest dry-bulb temperature reading across the top. The number where the two columns meet is the relative humidity. In this example, it is 48%.

2. Predicting Forest Fire Danger

Forest fire danger is caused by several weather conditions. The wind speed indicates how fast forest fires will spread; the amount of moisture in the air (relative humidity) tells how dry or wet the air is and the fuel moisture indicates the dryness of the fuel (dead branches, duff, brush, etc., in the forest).

General forest fire danger forecasts can be based on the following observations:

Observations	Forecast
High temperature (70° F), high winds, low relative humidity (below 30) low fuel moisture	High fire danger
Moderate winds, low relative humidity, low fuel moisture	Medium fire danger
No wind, low relative humidity, low fuel moisture	Medium fire danger
High winds, medium relative humidity, high fuel moisture	High fire danger
Rain, high fuel moisture, low temperature (below 60°)	Low fire danger

3. Weather Proverbs

When you give your weather forecast, it will be interesting to conclude your report with a weather proverb. Here are a few proverbs for different forecasts.

Fair weather

When the dew is on the grass
Rain will never come to pass.

The higher the clouds,
The finer the weather

Storm Approaching

When the grass is dry at morning's light
Look for rain before the night.

When high clouds and low clouds do not march together,
Prepare for a blow and a change in the weather.

A ring around the sun or moon
Brings rain or snow upon you soon.

Dark clouds in the west
Stay indoors and rest.

Bad Weather is Here

When clouds move down and turn dark grey
A rainy spell is on the way.

When teeth, bones and bunions ache,
Expect the clouds to fill a lake.

Clearing Weather

The weather will clear when there is enough blue sky to make a pair of Dutchman's breeches.

Welcome the sound of crackling hair
It tells of weather clear and fair.

General Proverb When You Can't Make Up Your Mind

When the wind's in the south,
The rain's in his mouth.
When the smoke goes west,
Bad weather is past.
When smoke goes east,
Bad weather is next.
When the smoke is from the north,
Good weather will come forth.

4. Weather Flags

You might like to make and display the weather flag of your weather prediction. The following chart shows the color of flag to be flown with your weather forecast.

WEATHER FLAGS		
Flag	Color	Meaning
	All white	Fair weather
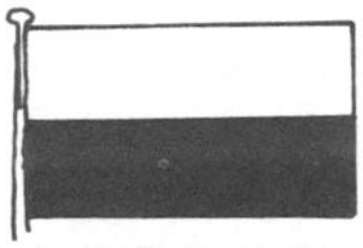	Top white Bottom blue	Local showers or snow flurries
	All blue	Rain or snow
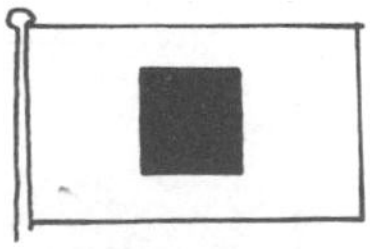	White with blue center	Cold wave
	Black	Above the flag-warmer weather Below the flag-cooler weather

B. GENERAL WEATHER FORECAST INDICATOR CHART

Type of Weather Predicted	Temperature	Air Pressure	Rainfall	Humidity	Wind Direction	Wind Speed	Cloud
FAIR WEATHER INDICATORS (High Pressure Area)	Warm or rising	Steady or rising	None	Usually low or decreasing in P.M.	Shifting NW, N, NE in summer	Gentle	High clouds or some towering clouds. Morning fog decreasing by noon. Frost in morning.
STORM INDICATORS (Low Pressure Area)	Low or decreasing in summer. Rising in winter.	Dropping	Increasing	High	S to W winds all year. E winds in winter can bring snow, freezing rain.	Moderate to Increasing	Middle clouds; darkening skies in S and W. Ring around sun and moon. Clouds thin. Drop in elevation.
CLEARING WEATHER INDICATORS	Rising	Rising	Decreasing	Decreasing	NW to N winds, all year. Also East in summer.	Moderate to Decreasing	Rising and broken clouds.

GENERAL WEATHER FORECAST INDICATOR CHART FOR ____________________
(Describe Your Area)

Type of Weather Predicted	Temperature	Air Pressure	Rainfall	Humidity	Wind Direction	Wind Speed	Clouds

C. DAILY WEATHER DATA AND FORECAST CHART

A.M. FORECAST			Time: A.M.	P.M. FORECAST			Time: P.M.
Temperature:			Weather Forecast:	Temperature:			Weather Forecast:
Air Pressure: (Rising or Falling)				Air Pressure: (Rising or Falling)			
Rainfall:				Rainfall:			
Humidity:			Fire Danger Forcast: (circle One) LOW MEDIUM HIGH	Humidity:			Fire Danger Forecast: (Circle One) LOW MEDIUM HIGH
Wind Speed:			Weather Flag:	Wind Speed:			Weather Flag:
Direction:	Upper	Lower	Weather Proverb:	Direction:	Upper	Lower	Weather Proverb:
Cloud Formation & Symbol: Upper				Cloud Formation & Symbol: Upper			
Lower				Lower			

D. HOW DOES WEATHER AFFECT:

Plants? ____________________

Soil? ____________________

Water? ____________________

Animals? ____________________

Man? ____________________

Predict the weather daily, taking your readings at the same time each day. Record your observations on the weather and data sheet.

E. A LIST OF WEATHER WORDS

<u>Anemometer</u> - An instrument used to measure the exact wind speed in miles per hour.

<u>Barometer</u> - An instrument used to record air pressure. It weighs the total column of air that is pressing down on a given area at a certain time.

<u>Condensation</u> - The process of changing vapor from invisible to visible moisture.

<u>Dewpoint</u> - The temperature at which vapor changes to visible moisture such as fog, dew, or rain.

<u>Evaporation</u> - The process of changing vapor from visible to invisible moisture.

<u>Meteorologist</u> - A person trained in the science of the atmosphere; one who studies weather and climate.

<u>Precipitation</u> - - Cloud droplets that fall to the earth as rain, snow, hail and sleet. Precipitation is reported by the amount of liquid which falls in a given length of time.

<u>Psychrometer</u> - An instrument used to measure relative humidity.

<u>Rain Gauge</u> - An instrument used to measure the amount of precipitation that falls in a given period of time.

<u>Relative Humidity</u> - The amount of water vapor (in percent) that the air can hold at a given temperature compared with the amount it could hold before it rains.

<u>Temperature</u> - The degree of hotness or coldness of the atmosphere, usually as measured on a thermometer.

<u>Weather</u> - The condition of our atmosphere in relation to pressure, wind, heat and moisture present.

F. SUGGESTED SPECIAL INTEREST PROJECTS

1. Record local weather observations on the weather data and forecast chart in the manual.
2. Record some general weather forecast indicators for your area on the chart in the manual.
3. Correlate tree leader growth and tree ring count with past records of rainfall and growing seasons to see if weather had any effect on tree growth.
4. Compose a song about the sounds of the wind in the trees.
5. Compose a poem about the weather.
6. Write a story describing the clouds that bring thunderstorms and lightning.
7. Paint a picture of the clouds seen over your field study area and describe what weather they indicate.
8. Take pictures of different cloud formations.

Date: ______________________

Time of Day: ________________

Weather: ___________________

G. DATA SHEET FOR SPECIAL INTEREST PROJECTS

Description of Project:

Recorded Data, Observations & Conclusions:

Date: ____________________

Time of Day: ____________________

Weather: ____________________

DATA SHEET FOR SPECIAL INTEREST PROJECTS

Description of Project:

Recorded Data, Observations & Conclusions:

Date: ______________________________

Time of Day: ______________________

Weather: __________________________

DATA SHEET FOR SPECIAL INTEREST PROJECTS

Description of Project:

Recorded Data, Observations & Conclusions: